THE FEVER BARK TREE

The
FEVER BARK TREE

The Pageant of Quinine

BY M. L. DURAN-REYNALS

 DOUBLEDAY & COMPANY, INC.
GARDEN CITY, NEW YORK
1946

ACKNOWLEDGMENTS

I wish to acknowledge with the deepest gratitude the editorial assistance of Miss Madeline Stanton, secretary of the Historical Library, Yale School of Medicine, who patiently purged this manuscript from foreign expressions and constructions. I also want to thank Mrs. Samuel H. Fredericks, Jr., reference librarian of the Sterling Library, for her invaluable help; Mrs. Eugene V. Rostow for advice and support; Dr. Morris Tager for technical guidance; and the staffs of the Historical Library, of the Yale School of Medicine, and of the Sterling Library of Yale University for their continuous assistance.

PREFACE

Anyone who has been on the plains of the Roman Campagna and gazed at the temple at Paestum standing alone in the swampy wastelands of southern Italy as an impressive reminder of an earlier civilization, cannot fail to appreciate the importance of malaria in shaping national destinies. A Greek colony founded about 600 B.C. at Paestum flourished for some three hundred years, when the entire area, perhaps from faulty irrigation, became overrun with fever; in the belief that such agues had their origin in the bad air (*mal-aria*), the colonists fled the humid plains for the more invigorating air of the higher terrain, but they left behind them the great Temple of Neptune, one of the finest specimens of the golden age of Greek art.

The impact of malaria on history, and particularly upon military history, has never been fully described, but popular interest has become so great in the course of the recent World War that the public has rightly begun to demand an authoritative account of the disease and all its ramifications, historical and otherwise. It is conservatively estimated that three hundred million people in the world are now victims of malaria. In India alone one out of every four persons is afflicted, i.e., approximately one hundred million persons, two million of whom die each year from the disease—more than the total deaths from all causes in the United States. So important did the problem grow for our armed forces in the Pacific that malaria control became as essential to a military victory as offensive weapons. Indeed it was our success in stemming the spread of malaria, and in controlling the disease once it had been acquired, that contributed as much as any single circumstance to our military success in the Pacific Theater. In 1943 the Army and Navy created, with the co-operation of the National Research Council, the Board for the Co-ordination of Malarial Studies which in less than three years succeeded not only in instituting effective measures for control of malaria in the field but also in launching a formidable research program on the anti-malarials, in the course of which nearly eight thousand separate compounds were subjected to therapeutic test. From this large group of potentially effective drugs have emerged several which will replace both quinine itself and its well-known substitute, atabrine. So the story told in this volume is one that appropriately inaugurates a new period in the history not only of malariology but of medicine itself.

Mrs. Duran-Reynals has given us an engaging description of the struggle for recognition of quinine, the one therapeutic agent that until recently had been found effective in checking the ravages of the dread disease. She presents the more romantic historical details in direct and vigorous language without burdening the text with documentation. For those who wish the sources, however, she has provided at the end an excellent bibliography which includes many obscure and little-known primary sources. The story of human credulity, of prejudice and resistance to change, is poignantly unfolded in the narrative. To those who every day are confronted with the problem of passing upon some new therapeutic agent—be it a nostrum or a drug with a solid scientific basis—it is wise

PREFACE

to recall the long and bitter struggle of cinchona and attempt, while still exercising their best critical faculties, to remain completely openminded lest they overlook, as has happened so many times in the past, an agent such as penicillin which would be an everlasting boon to mankind.

The medical profession is under public scrutiny now, more so than at any time in its history, since our rapidly changing social structure is making greater and more varied demands upon the physician than ever before. For many reasons this is welcome, but certain demands have been unreasonable and they arise from basic lack of understanding of the physician's problems. Probably the best way in which the lay public can achieve a sympathetic knowledge of the medical profession is through medical biography and the study of the historical backgrounds of medicine. The story of quinine represents a highly significant phase of medical history, and we are much in Mrs. Duran-Reynals's debt for having laid it before us so vividly.

JOHN F. FULTON

Yale University
March 1946

CONTENTS

CHAPTER I

Of Fevers

In the year 336 B.C. there lived a young King of Macedonia who was destined to become the great hero of antiquity. His name was Alexander and he was of extreme beauty. He dressed like a pagan god and "his body was so fragrant as to perfume the clothes he wore next to his skin."

To these graces of body Alexander joined an alert mind and a great desire for learning which was satisfied in a manner worthy of kings by his mentor, the supreme Aristotle. Thus at an age when others would spend their time in the pursuit of amusement Alexander spent his in the study of philosophy, history, literature, and medicine, which he knew sufficiently well to practice on occasion. So much learning, however, did not turn Alexander into the aloof scholar, for he was made of the fiber of the warrior and the statesman; and a great dream of conquests took hold of the King of Macedonia. He wanted to unite all the peoples of his part of the world in a great political unit, to stop their constant fighting with each other, to create a great Asiatic empire, whose lifeblood would be the Greek culture Aristotle had spread out before him and which he so greatly admired.

Alexander was a born leader and everyone, soldier and scholar alike, joined him in the execution of this fantastic project, which began with the conquest of Greece, achieved when he was only twenty-one. Immediately thereafter he undertook the conquest of Persia. When the moment of decisive encounter with Darius, King of the Persians, arrived, no one doubted that victory would come to the twenty-two-year-old general. One very hot day, when the army was advancing by the side of the river toward the enemy, Alexander suddenly decided to refresh himself in its waters. He threw himself into the cold stream and immediately it became apparent that he was sinking. The cry went up that the king had lost consciousness. His soldiers rushed to his rescue and laid him on the grass. They looked at him, and what they saw filled them with despair. Alexander was deadly pale, cold perspiration covered his forehead, and he was shivering with a violent chill which made his arms and legs shake and his teeth chatter. It was the "horror," the curse, the evil—the unmistakable horror which preceded the terrible fever that would go higher and higher until, having reached its peak, it would disappear in a few hours, leaving him drenched in perspiration, so weak and exhausted that for days he would be indifferent to everything, until little by little he recovered. But Alexander was doomed: the horror was implacable; it always came back until it killed its victim.

It was all over the land, this horror, particularly in Greece, in the marshy districts where there was water, that indispensable element of agriculture. One person after another fell victim to it. Again and again they shivered and shook. Again and again they recovered, but each recovery took longer; their eyes sank, they looked paler and more emaciated, and their bellies swelled. Relentlessly the horror destroyed their bodies and also their patrimony, because it was during the warm season that attacks were worst and most frequent: the dreaded summer fever came when all hands were needed for the harvest. Eventually their minds withered; between attacks they would lie inert, seeing their land go to waste, their cattle untended, their houses falling about them, their wives and children hungry; but most of the children would die anyway. They were too exhausted to care.

This was the reason why in Greece, the core of that conglomeration of peoples that Alexander wanted to unite in a great empire, some of the richest lands were inhabited by the most wretched beings on earth. The fevers stopped armies, chased people from one land to another, ruined prosperous towns; the rich and the intelligent sought healthier homes, leaving behind the poor, the weak, and the unenterprising. They were powerless: no charm, herb, or incantation could placate the horror, which was carried by the mists over the stagnant waters in the hot, moist lands. This was the great demoniacal force of the ancient world which described hell as a huge marsh whence issued dense vapors saturated with the infernal miasma while the damned, with sunken eyes, green faces, and swollen bellies, turned round and round, shivering and shaking in eternal agony.

And now even Alexander had the horror. With the high fever he was thrown into a state of great agitation; he was delirious and unable to sleep. Later he became greatly depressed, lost his voice, and for a while lay in a comatose condition. Nature, however, is a great healer when youth and strength are on its side. Alexander survived this time; and, disregarding the bad omen, he conquered Egypt and Persia within the next ten years and started the invasion of India. He was thirty-two years old; his mind and body had reached their full maturity and vigor. He was King of Asia; the great political unit of his dreams was a reality. But on the third day of June of the year 323 B.C. Alexander woke up with a fever in the small hours of the morning. The horror had come back. Nine days later his soldiers, forcing their way to his tent, demanded to see their captain. One by one they marched past the bed where lay the King of Asia, his violet eyes wide open, gazing fixedly into space, as quiet as a statue, unable to speak and probably unaware of this last tribute of his men. Late in the afternoon of the next day, the eleventh of his disease, Alexander died. The empire that was in the making burst into fragments like a fallen star, leaving to future generations nothing but the radiant light of the Alexandrine legend.

About the time when Alexander was born in Macedonia a man in Greece named Hippocrates from the island of Cos was explaining to the learned world of his day what fevers were. And when Hippocrates talked of fevers he talked mainly of the horror, the great disease of his country, which he called the intermittent fever, or the tertian or the quartan, depending on whether the attack came every other day or every fourth day. To him and to his pupils this was the disease of primary importance, influencing their concept of all other ailments. Hippocrates placed the greatest importance on the change of the seasons as the main cause of all diseases because the intermittent fevers were obviously influenced by changes in temperature, the rains, and even the direction in which the winds blew.

Fevers, according to Hippocrates, were the result of the separation in the body of the elements of heat and cold; and so he said: "So long as the hot and the cold in the body are mixed together, they cause no pain. For the hot is tempered and moderated by the cold, and the cold by the hot. But when either is entirely separated from the other, then it causes pain." The manner in which these elements of heat and cold became separated was the work of the four humors: blood, phlegm, yellow bile, and black bile. Too much blood or too little bile would disturb the proper balance and sickness would ensue. Thus the humor causing the disease would become the "corrupt humor" within the body. In order to destroy or expel it, nature would bring about a process of fermentation of the blood which caused a rise in temperature, hence fever. Of the four humors, bile seems to have been the most damaging when altered; at least Hippocrates concludes that: "All fevers come from the bile."

These alterations in the balance of the humors seem to have been very much influenced by the elements: "air, earth, fire, and water." According to the school of Cos, of these four elements air could become the most noxious, by virtue of its unlimited power. Air filled the universe, brought about the change of seasons, kept the sun, moon, and stars in motion, moved the oceans; the earth floated on air. Air was eternal in time and infinite in space. Air, therefore, was the main agent of disease because, unlike fire, earth, or water, it could penetrate the whole organism. So well established became the idea of the power of evil air that two thousand years after Hippocrates' time the intermittent fevers became universally known by the Italian words for "bad air"—malaria.

These explanations, presented in a far more elaborate way, remained the basis of all medical speculation on the origin of diseases in the occidental world until the nineteenth century. In Hippocrates' time they had the enormous merit of establishing the mechanisms of disease on rational terms; a rational mechanism, no matter how vague and farfetched, was better than a supernatural one, and it was a decisive advance in our culture.

Hippocrates' explanations, brilliant as they were, did not

check the fevers of Greece. As a matter of fact it was after his time that Greece decayed with incredible rapidity, and it has been many times postulated that the widespread intermittent fevers had a great share in the process. To what extent they prevailed is shown by Aristotle's statement, "As the moon is called the cause of a solar eclipse, so fatigue is the cause of fever." Fevers must indeed have been an everyday occurrence to be attributed to so common an agent as fatigue. But whatever the cause, in the second century B.C. Greece became practically depopulated. Political factions and loss of commercial supremacy due to the rising power of Rome may have been the main factors in its final collapse; yet the relative rapidity with which this collapse took place seems to suggest a cause far swifter in its mechanism than the workings of power politics.

Of all Greek institutions of the past, Hippocrates' school of medical thought fared worst in the widespread decay of the country. The people in general returned to their superstitious practices in their ailments and Hippocrates' rationalizations were forgotten. Again it has been suggested that the fevers were the main cause of this attitude. The country was corroded by a disease against which the physicians of the Hippocratic School were powerless. They told the sick man to keep away from magic and witchcraft because his fever was caused by an imbalance of the humors that no witch could cure; but neither could they. And the sick man in his distress looked for mental comfort in the promises of recovery given to him by unscrupulous oracles and medicine men.

The few believers in the rational causes of disease left the country and went to Alexandria in Egypt, where a wise Ptolemy had created one of the greatest schools of antiquity.

However, in Alexandria the great medical authority, Erasistratus, ignoring the balance of the humors, maintained that fevers were caused by the blood going into the veins and arteries, which should contain only air. Consequently as a remedy he recommended and practiced binding of the veins and arteries to stop the passage of the noxious blood. How this treatment was accomplished is difficult to visualize unless the patient was reduced to the condition of an Egyptian mummy. The Greek physicians eventually migrated to Rome, capital of the new empire, some directly, some by way of Alexandria.

It did not take long for the old enemy to follow in their tracks. In Rome also the mists and fogs that arose from the marshes carried the malignant miasma. Here also the physicians endeavored to explain the causes of the fevers while trying to stop their ever increasing prevalence. One named Petron, with a sadistic turn of mind, would smother his patients with clothes while forbidding them any sort of drink as long as the fever lasted. Another, a magnificent charlatan with the high-sounding name of Asclepiades, devised a theory that atoms, by obstructing the pores, produced the various fevers, the little atoms being the cause of the tertian and the big atoms of the quartan. Still another, named Andromachus, recommended a concoction of everlasting fame called the theriac, composed of sixty-one ingredients, which was supposed to cure the fevers instantly. In the first century B.C. Dioscorides recommended fleas for the fevers, whereas Pliny the Younger recommended eyes, both of crabs and wolves, together with vipers. But the greatest of all, named Galen, following in Hippocrates' footsteps, also speculated on the balance of the humors and the evil effects of the bile; and as treatment he strongly recommended that the fever should be helped in its endeavor to free the body from malignant humors by the unlimited use of purging and bleeding.

It was all of no avail; as in Greece, the fevers of Rome could not be stopped. Neither fleas nor wolves nor crabs could bring relief to the sick man, not even the great Galen, with all his purging and bleeding. The Greek medical theories helped the Romans no more than they had helped the Greeks themselves. And the Romans, who were practical people and knew power when they saw it, though greatly admiring the wisdom of Greece, made fever a goddess. To her three sanctuaries were built in the city of Rome. By worship and sacrifices the Romans tried to avert the great destroyer of men, but neither flattery nor bribery could abate the horror. For centuries the poisonous emanations of the Pontine Marshes decimated the agricultural population of the Roman Campagna and kept the inhabitants of the city of Rome in constant terror.

Long before Galen was born, Cato the censor, who disliked Greek physicians, had settled the problem of fevers: he recommended cabbage for their treatment; and if this wonderful remedy should fail, he emphatically and wisely declared, the fight against the summer fevers was useless. Long after Galen was dead, the recital of Homer's *Iliad* to the patient was prescribed as a remedy for the quartan fever.

The Roman Empire fell; political strife, demoralization of customs, foreign invasions, all contributed to its downfall. Notwithstanding all this, a very important role in the collapse of this great political unit has been ascribed to the intermittent fevers, which depopulated some of the most important agricultural areas of Italy.

Europe entered the Middle Ages. The Christian religion had destroyed the old pagan beliefs and Rome became the capital of Christendom. The Christian believer, however, was as helpless as the pagan Roman to cope with the fevers that raged in the Eternal City. Roman churches were built to Our Lady of the Fevers. In spite of this scourge Rome became the coveted prize of the barbaric princes of the north who, escaping the cold regions, were lured by the sunny lands of wine and honey only to pay for the mad gesture with their lives. In the fifth century A.D. Alaric was the first barbarian conqueror to enter Rome. He chose to storm the city during the summer solstice, and the summer fever avenged itself by taking his life. Again and again the Germanic hordes invaded Rome either to die or to leave it in haste, haunted by the horror. The same fate befell the Lombards, the Franks, and later on the Spaniards.

With the general collapse of scientific speculation that took place in the Middle Ages, medicine was no longer a learned profession and the art of healing was left to herb sellers, old women, and fortunetellers. No Hippocrates, no Galen, tried to evolve complicated, scientific theories as to the cause of the fevers of Rome. As a matter of fact no one seemed to care whether they had any cause at all; man was born to die, this life was the temporary vehicle to a better one, and a fever was as good a way as any of getting it over with. The seventh century saw the beginning of monastic medicine, which made some effort to preserve the learning of the past, but the early monastic scholars were likewise imbued with the prevailing spirit of despondency, at least so far as fevers were concerned. An English monk, the Venerable Bede, described "the nature of fevers" by dwelling on the true health which is given by God, by affirming that after the "impurity and iniquity of man's flesh which brings forth death" there will be eternal life. Then he discusses the many demons of disease and ends by quoting Luke on the subject of miracles. And this is all we know about fevers from the Venerable Bede. The remedies of the time were in line with Bede's philosophy of disease: prayers, exorcisms, amulets, and the ministrations of holy men who lived in solitude and meditation, practicing mortification of the flesh.

By the eleventh century the German princes had renounced the conquest of Rome, or rather the idea of living in Rome. The Eternal City was left to the Holy See; but the princes of the Church also paid a heavy tribute to the fevers for remaining there. Peter Cardinal Damian about 1060 described the dangers of Rome in the following verses:

Rome, voracious of men, breaks down the strongest human nature.
Rome, hot bed of fevers, is an ample giver of the fruits of death.
The Roman fevers are faithful according to an imprescriptable right:
Whom once they have touched, they do not abandon as long as he lives.

And Peter Cardinal Damian was far from indulging in hyperbole. Popes and cardinals died in staggering numbers. When a pope died the foreign cardinals who had to attend the conclave in Rome to choose his successor were in constant fear while they remained in the city. So distracted were their minds by the idea of the disease that these conclaves became the occasion for all varieties of hysterical scenes. In the year 1241 a new pope had to be elected; the cardinals had scarcely begun the customary deliberations when one of their number died. Such terror seized the others that they were unable to reach a decision. Finally Celestine IV was elected, but he himself died fifteen days later and the cardinals fled in panic from the unburied body of the new pope. At the conclave of

1287, which lasted ten months, six cardinals died and the rest fled the city. When one realizes that during the thirteenth century seventeen popes died and consequently seventeen such conclaves took place, with all their attendant strife and sudden deaths, it is perhaps small wonder that the Church began to show signs of dissension that ended in the great schism of the fifteenth century.

The fourteenth century began under no better auspices for the Vatican than the thirteenth. Two popes had already died by 1305; Clement V was elected in that year, and in 1309 he decided to move the papal court to Avignon in France. Political reasons have been given for this decision of the pontiff, although there is good evidence to show that the fear of the Roman air was the real cause for the apparent obstinacy of popes and cardinals to remain at Avignon. In 1367 Urban V decided to return to Rome, where he remained for three years though he never stayed in the city from spring to autumn. In September 1370 he went back to Avignon; three months later he died and according to Petrarch his cardinals had poisoned him because they were terrified that he might want to move the papal court back to the Eternal City. It may be that Petrarch's accusations had no more ground than his own apprehensions of a disease he knew much too well. "My faithful Tertian," he wrote, "and September, my constant enemy, conspired so well to my detriment that if they had been, the former somewhat stronger, the latter somewhat longer, they would certainly have made away with me"; which they probably did in the course of time as they did with another illustrious Italian, Dante Alighieri, who also died of fevers in the fourteenth century.

The popes resided in Avignon for sixty-eight years, during

which time six of their number had died as compared to twelve who had died in Rome during a similar interval in the preceding century. This fact was the more remarkable as it was while the popes lived in Avignon that the Black Death swept over Europe, killing half its population. Clement VI was pope when the plague struck Avignon. His physician, Guy de Chauliac, confined him to his rooms in complete isolation and he survived the terrible pandemic. De Chauliac was a great physician who had a premonition as to how the plague was propagated; all his precautions, however, would have been of no avail if he had tried to save the pope from the fevers of Rome. Had he kept the pontiff in his rooms at the Vatican, deprived of human contact for the rest of his life, the fevers would have reached him just the same, and Guy de Chauliac with all his reasoning would never have guessed how it had happened.

European medicine in the thirteenth century returned to the theories of the Greek School, mainly through the influence of an Arabian physician named Avicenna, who had revived in all its complexity the theory of the humors. With oriental magnificence Avicenna, known as the prince of physicians, recommended gold, silver, and precious stones to purify the blood from the corrupt humors, cause of the fevers, and started the fashion of pills colored with gold and silver dyes. European physicians learned once more that fevers were caused by too much blood or too little bile, and the impact was felt by even the monastic authorities. About the middle of the century Bartholomaeus Anglicus, a Franciscan monk of the noble house of Suffolk, writing about fevers in somewhat poetical terms, said: "A fever is strange heate kindeled in the hearts and comes out thereof, by means of spirits and of blood, into all the body and burns thereof and that burning grieves the works of kinde." Then he proceeds to say that as man's body is made of three things—"subtle things as of spirits, fleeting things as of humors, and bodily things as of the members"—so there are three diverse kinds of fevers. The first, called "ephimera," is like hot wine in a bottle, which heats the bottle; the second, called "putrid," is like hot water in a vessel; the third, called "ethica," is like cold water in a hot vessel: it takes the heat from it. This theory, though not reaching the speculative heights of Hippocrates and Galen, was a great step forward from Bede's mystical confusions.

The remedies for fevers had also departed from purely religious ceremonies. Albertus Magnus, the celebrated Dominican teacher of Thomas Aquinas, is said to have recommended two particularly infallible ones. The first was called a remedy of sympathy because it acted at a distance from the sick man: "Take the urine of the patient and mix it with some flour to make a good dough thereof, of which seventy-seven small cakes are made: proceed before sunrise to an ant hill and throw the cakes therein. As soon as the insects have devoured the cakes the fever vanishes." The author assures the reader that its great value has been amply tested. The other remedy, to be administered directly, was one by which a lady of high birth had been able to aid many a feverish person. According to Albertus Magnus, "this matron of a noble family cut the ear of a cat, let three drops of the blood fall in some brandy, added a little pepper thereto, and gave it to the patient to drink"; the effect was miraculous.

In the fifteenth century a colorful genius named Aureolus Philippus Theophrastus Bombastus von Hohenheim, who called himself Paracelsus, decided that diseases were caused by chemical changes within the body and, ignoring the humor-chasing Galenists, introduced as remedies the use of mineral substances, such as sulphuric acid, preparations of mercury compounds, and some mysterious concoction he called the philosophers' stone. A violent controversy arose between the pro-chemical followers of Paracelsus and the pro-humor followers of Galen; under different names and in a more subdued form this controversy still rages. Paracelsus with his simple chemicals undoubtedly took the first salutary step toward freeing medicine from the complicated compounds of the Arabians and Romans. As far as the cure of fevers was concerned, however, Paracelsus's chemicals were as much a failure as the purging and bleeding of the Galenists. Evading the issue, he recommended for their treatment the use of talismans and magic procedures; in his chaotic mind, along with his belief in chemistry, he also set great store by a form of mysticism closely akin to witchcraft.

The Galenists meanwhile got the best of the argument and by the sixteenth century the theory of the humors was so well established that a physician of the time dared to make the sweeping statement that humors and not bad angels were the cause of disease. Yet, when it came to fevers as such, he weakened and admitted that the devil could mingle with the humors and so produce fevers that had no apparent cause and which could be cured only by confidence in Christ.

Confidence in divine help was certainly needed, for in the sixteenth century appeared the first report that malaria, then known as the ague, had spread all over the Continent. By the seventeenth century the ague was the great disease of Europe. In 1618 Sir Walter Raleigh mounted the scaffold, praying in agony that the attack of ague, due at any time, would not come lest his shaking and shivering might be attributed by the people to cowardice in the face of death. In the year 1639 a malignant fever raged so fiercely in England during the harvest time that there was danger of losing the crops for lack of hands.

Wherever there were stagnant waters—lakes, marshes, or swamps—wherever climatic conditions allowed a temperature high enough for minute organisms to breed, the ague attacked people of all ages and races. Consequently it is not surprising that the fashionable recorders of the seventeenth century, like Evelyn, Pepys, Saint-Simon, and Mme. de Sévigné, should dwell most particularly on the subject of fevers. These indefatigable gossipers commented on their friends' fevers, speculating on whether they suffered from the tertian, the quartan, the semitertian, or the double tertian; they discussed remedies for fevers, recommending to each other some particularly effective ones, such as plasters, herbs, infusions, and cordials; and they also appraised the ability of famous physicians according to their skill in treating fevers, whether they bled and purged the patient before, after, or during the attack.

A peculiarity of the ague is that when the fever attack takes place a considerable number of blood corpuscles are destroyed; thus if the patient was bled, the loss of blood was a serious one and the result was acute anemia. But in the seventeenth century and long afterward bled they were, anemic they became— and Galen be praised.

Another procedure for the treatment of the ague, very popular at the time, was astrology, which throughout the ages had been closely connected with this disease. The attacks seemed to follow a more or less precise pattern: in some patients they began always at the same hour and ended at the same hour. All this strongly suggested that an exact mechanism was at the root of the disease, and nothing could be more exact than the movement of the planets and the stars. The Romans believed that the Dog Star, Sirius, brightest of the fixed stars, increased the virulence of the fevers because it was during the so-called dog days, from July fifteenth to August twentieth, when Sirius showed above the horizon at the same time of day as the sun, that the fevers were most prevalent in Rome.

Eventually a system was worked out by which the course of the fever could be diagnosed by ascertaining the planetary influences under which the patient had been born. This diagnosis, however, was a very complicated process with the quarters of the moon and the tides of the ocean thrown in, and it required very involved astrological calculations that only astrologers could work out. It was a rather easy way of making a living; the whole thing was quite harmless and the sick man learned a fair amount of astronomy in the process.

Astrology, however, had one handicap: when it came to the treatment of the disease, all the celestial forces were powerless to mitigate the fever. Once the patient knew that Venus or Mars or both were the cause of his fever the astrologer lost his client. The point then was to extend the period of diagnosis, to make as difficult and as long as possible the procedure by which the cause of the fever was to be discovered. A resourceful man named Blagrave found the solution to the problem. In the year 1670 he published a book of astrology in which he rightly states that medicine had failed to cure the ague, since there were as many remedies as there were people with the disease; and in certain cases even astrology itself could fail. But then it was a case of witchcraft. The only way to cure the

fever was by finding the witch; and he, Blagrave, was unique
at finding witches, also by means of astrological calculations.
He cautioned particularly against the nurse, because the perseverance of the fever pointed strongly toward somebody near
the patient. To strengthen his theory he described a particular
case of persistent fevers in which the patient was attended by
a young maid who was always laughing. The stars told him
to mistrust this jolly creature and it was found that not only
was she a witch but that her mother and her grandmother had
also been witches. Blagrave explains that once the witch had
been found she had to be "afflicted." It is well known how
witches were afflicted in the seventeenth century, and it gives
one a slight heartache to think of the fate that befell the laughing young girl of Blagrave's clinical history. Astrology was no
longer a harmless superstition.

Besides bleeding, purging, astrology, and witch-hunting
there were in the seventeenth century an infinite number of
remedies for the ague. But the ague was no exception because
the pharmacopoeia of the time was incredibly prolific; everything from an old shoe to a dead rat had some particular
virtue and cured something or other. However, with the ague
things appear to have gone a little too far. Consequently a Dr.
White, in an attempt to expose the useless medicines employed
in the treatment of fevers, attacked particularly a certain Dr.
Goddard's Drops. It seems that these drops were prepared
from human skulls, and Dr. White justly points out that one
cannot be sure but that the skull used was that of a "pocky"
person; that is, a person afflicted with pustules or suffering
from syphilis. Dr. White was a cautious man and he was also
adamant against another medicine made of mummy; for the
mummy while alive might have been leprous, pocky, itchy, or

scrofulous. Dr. White insisted on blood-letting in the treatment of fevers and would not tolerate medicines other than crabs' eyes mixed with radishes, occasionally and with moderation.

Ever since the horror killed Alexander the Great in the prime of life the men who have made our culture have had to cope incessantly with the most insidious of all diseases. It hampered agriculture, trade, exploration, and colonial enterprises. Whether it was already on the American continent before the Spaniards came or whether the conquistadors brought it themselves is not known. It is believed, however, that early pre-Columbian civilizations, like that of the Mayas in Mexico, had been destroyed by malaria, and it was to escape the disease that the early Spanish colonists built their larger cities at high altitudes: Mexico City, La Paz in Bolivia, Bogotá in Colombia, Quito in Ecuador, and so many others. But Buenos Aires in Argentina owes its lovely name and no doubt its early prosperity to the absence of malaria. In the seventeenth century the ague had already ravaged the Indian populations and every viceroy and government official was afflicted by it. This was not a dramatic disease like the Black Death; the Black Death came, killed, and left, and the survivors kept on in the path of human progress. The ague never came and never left; it was always there. Nobody remembered how it began, nobody remembered that it ever disappeared once it had found its way into the country. It did not kill in a few days, like the Black Death; it killed after years of succeeding attacks which maimed its victim physically and mentally, making material progress impossible.

For centuries man was powerless against this disease; there was nothing he could do for its prevention because he did not have the faintest idea of its cause, and there was nothing that he could do for its treatment because the only medicine that could cure it was to be found in a part of the world that he did not even know existed. To free him of this scourge a New World had to be discovered and in the impenetrable forests of this New World, where millions of trees of infinite varieties grew, a certain tree had to be found, whose bark contained the precious remedy. According to a great Italian physician the introduction of this bark was of the same importance to medicine that the discovery of gunpowder was to the art of war. Yet when in the seventeenth century the extraordinary discovery was made, the use of this unique remedy was bitterly opposed in the name of a medical theory elaborated two thousand years before.

How this remedy was found, how its use was opposed, how this opposition was overcome by the combined efforts of a group of great men, how the remedy proved to be as important to medicine as gunpowder was to the art of war, and how its production and distribution are still today a burning issue is the history of quinine. It is a tale of hatred, greed, prejudice, generosity, and heroism; it is not a new tale because man, who is a monotonous animal, fights against his own salvation every time opportunity affords itself. But it is an unfinished tale and by making it known it is hoped that someone someday will find for it a happy ending, because the horror of Alexander, the intermittent fevers of Hippocrates, the ague of the Middle Ages, and the malaria of our day still pose a problem to be solved in that extensive part of the world where, in the twentieth century, agriculture, trade, and industry are carried on as in the time when Abram left Ur of the Chaldees to barter his wares with the Haranites and the Canaanites.

CHAPTER II

The Countess's Powder

A viceroy of Peru was returning to Spain in the year 1641, having served faithfully for ten years the interests of the Spanish Crown in her immense dominions in the New World. He had been rewarded, on leaving his post, with the rank of admiral of the Spanish Armada, and still more honors were presumably waiting for him at the court in Madrid. Neither honors nor wealth, however, were of much consequence to this viceroy, who had been born to both. He was Don Luis Geronimo Cabrera de Bobadilla, fourth Count of Chinchón, a Spanish grandee who as an equal to his king could remain covered in his presence and be seated when the king was seated. The scion of two of the noblest houses of Aragon and Castile, he was descended in a straight line from the illustrious Cabreras of Catalonia and on his mother's side from the famous Beatriz de Bobadilla, the lifelong friend and confidante of Queen Isabella and therefore one of the major voices in the elaborate negotiations that led to the discovery of the New World. The fourth Count of Chinchón thus was a rich man because he was lord of Valdemoro and Casarubios and the feudal owner of the territories of Chinchón near Madrid. And he was a powerful man because he was the hereditary governor of the castles of Segovia, general treasurer of the Crown of Aragon, and member of the Council of Italy; all of which had been crowned by the viceregency of Peru, one of the most important positions in the Spanish Empire.

The returning viceroy was, therefore, not looking forward to the usual rewards which crown a successful political career, not only because he was a grandee of Spain and nothing could honor him further, but also because he wanted to retire from public life out of a deep sense of failure and disappointment, although to all appearances he had carried out his administrative duties most competently and to the great advantage of the Crown. However, in the light of a memoir he had written for his successor in the viceregency, giving an account of the conditions under which he was leaving the "Realms of Peru," it appeared that the efforts of the fourth Count of Chinchón had been directed not toward the great advantage of the Crown but toward the greater advantage of the American subjects of the Crown.

From the very beginning he had fallen in love with the New World, and his innate decency had revolted in righteous indignation against the abuses and depredations committed by his Spanish compatriots on the subjugated Indians, and against the indifference of Madrid toward these inexcusable abuses. Yet at first the Count of Chinchón had been happy in Lima, the capital of Peru, because colonial Lima of the seventeenth century was undoubtedly a city of great elegance, much learning, and unusual refinement.

The gaiety of its citizens was inexhaustible; bullfights, balls, plays, and parades were daily occurrences. In a constant spirit of celebration the whole town turned into a riotous occasion any event, such as the birth of a royal prince in Madrid, the nomination of a new public officer, or simply the arrival of the mail with news from the Old World. This exuberance of the citizens of Lima was, moreover, of the most unpredictable sort. There was a custom in the University of San Marcos according to which, when a chair was vacant, the aspiring professor had to read publicly a learned thesis on the subject to be taught, usually theology and philosophy. The citizenry never missed such occasions, and after the exercise the audience would indulge in violent debates as to who had given a better interpretation to the sacred arcana of St. Thomas Aquinas or St. Augustine.

The viceroy, who led a life of exemplary austerity, obviously favored a graver sort of behavior; but this had not detracted from his happiness, and on occasions he too had joined in the continuous carnival within the limits of his exalted dignity. In later years, however, the pitiful condition of the Peruvian Indians had become almost an obsession with him. One after another he had sent long and detailed memoranda to Madrid suggesting reforms for their welfare, and one after another they had been disregarded. He had sustained endless arguments with the advisers of the Crown in Peru and had accomplished practically nothing, his greater victories being an increase of a few cents a day in the salary of the mining Indians; a law forbidding the Indians to sell their homelands to the Spaniards in order to protect them from utter slavery; another law forcing the Spaniards to live by themselves fully aware of how dangerous on all accounts was their proximity to the helpless Indians. For a man whose goal had been to give the Indian full civil rights and to establish laws of commerce which, while protecting the merchants of Peru, would make for the prosperity of the New World, these were indeed negligible achievements.

He struggled, moreover, under an almost unbearable strain because he was a sick man, suffering from a severe case of malaria that he had contracted in Lima where, with all the gaiety, it was an inescapable curse. The periodic attacks of

fever, the frequency of which had increased alarmingly, finally
kept the viceroy in a constant state of prostration, greatly intensified by the continuous purging and bleeding to which he
was subjected by his physicians. As a result of all this he had
become embittered and in his resentment had developed an
uncommon hatred against the Spaniards in Peru, whom, in the
memoir for his successor, he described in forceful terms as a
plundering and despicable lot, whose presence in the New
World was quite unnecessary since the future greatness of the
new continent could be achieved only by the Indians themselves. He therefore warned the new viceroy against the Spaniards while entreating him to protect the interests, both material and spiritual, of the Indians, by leaving his doors wide open
to those who would defend them as he himself had always done.
The feeling of despondency which pervades the pages of this
memoir clearly shows that the Count of Chinchón felt as
though his ten years in Peru had been a vacuum in the history
of the New World.

On his way to Spain the count had to stop in Panama to wait
for the Spanish fleet to take him home with the honors due his
rank. While there, as a result of some epidemic, his wife, Doña
Francisca, Countess of Chinchón, died and was buried in the
city of Panama. With this final misfortune it is not hard to
imagine in what state of mind the viceroy completed his journey homeward, accompanied by his only son, eleven years of
age. They reached Spain in 1641. After spending in Madrid
the time strictly necessary to give the king an account of his
mission in Peru, the viceroy hastily withdrew with his son to
the castle of Chinchón. Surrounded by the ascetic solitude of
the barren lands of Castile, the viceroy, his thoughts on the
fruitful tropics beyond the sea, devoted himself exclusively

to the writing of a voluminous report, dedicated to the king and concerned with improving the administration of the "Realms of Peru." He was still working on it when, five years later, he died in comparative obscurity.

While the Count of Chinchón was struggling so intently for the improvement of a small sector of humanity, an event of the greatest importance to the welfare of the largest part of humanity had taken place in Lima. The first record of this event appeared in a religious book dealing with the chronicle of the Order of St. Augustine, written by an Augustinian monk by the name of Calancha before 1633 and published in Spain in 1639. In this book, quite independent of its religious content, the following paragraph appeared: "A tree grows which they call 'the fever tree' [*árbol de calenturas*] in the country of Loxa, whose bark, of the color of cinnamon, made into powder amounting to the weight of two small silver coins and given as a beverage, cures the fevers and tertianas; it has produced miraculous results in Lima." Thus simply and unassumingly did Father Calancha announce to the world that a cure had been found for the most widespread disease of the time. How this unique remedy had been found or how the Spaniards learned about it Father Calancha did not tell.

However, in later years this omission was richly compensated for by a variety of colorful versions. One account relates that certain Indians observed that ailing mountain lions would chew the bark of a particular tree, which turned out to be the fever tree. Another tells of a Spanish soldier who, seized with a fit of malaria in a deserted spot, drank from a nearby marsh and fell asleep. When he awoke the fever was gone. He remembered that the water had had a bitter taste and noticed that the trunk of a tree split by lightning had been submerged in it. That was the fever tree, whose anti-malarial substance had in the course of time become dissolved in the water. Still another version maintains that the Jesuits, who used to chew the bark of trees in order to differentiate them, were puzzled by the very bitter taste of this particular tree. Although the Society of Jesus later on played a decisive role in introducing the use of the bark into medicine, there is no evidence that the Jesuits were the first to recognize its medicinal virtues.

These fanciful versions seem to have sprung up because of the confusing fact that, according to reliable travelers in South America, the Peruvian Indians were ignorant of the medicinal virtues of the bark, which they refused to take even after it had become a universally accepted remedy. Yet considering the diversity of customs and beliefs which prevailed among the many Indian tribes that formed the Inca Empire, a more rational explanation would seem to be that only a small Indian group knew about the drug, which may even have been the secret of the tribe or perhaps of a single family. It also appears that certain drugs were reserved for the exclusive use of the Inca royal family and the high nobility, whose health was cared for by a group of official scholars, called Amautas, who were apparently great herbmen; and possibly the bark could have been one of these special remedies.

Moreover, a miraculous remedy found in Peru was not a unique happening. From the very beginning of its conquest the Spanish chroniclers had shown the greatest admiration for the natives' extensive knowledge of medicinal plants. These plants quickly found their way to Europe, and sixty years after the discovery of America an active commerce in curative plants was already established between the New and the Old Worlds by way of Spain. Innumerable herbs, resins, balsams, barks, and roots from Peru as well as from Mexico and Argentina were sent in Spanish galleons from the Indies to the port of Seville, and from there were distributed all over the Continent. Among these from Peru were such celebrities as the syrup of Tolú, balsam of Peru, sarsaparilla, chenopodium and coca leaves from which cocaine is extracted.

The Peruvian Indians were most dexterous in the preparation and use of their curative plants. Of one single plant, for instance, they used the young branches for cleaning the teeth and strengthening the gums; an infusion of the leaves for skin diseases; the fresh latex for ailments of the eyes; the dry latex to make plasters for wounds and to fill cavities in the teeth; the resin diluted in water as a laxative; the dry resin in suppository form for intestinal parasites; and an infusion of the bark for swelling of the legs.

So important and outstanding was the skill of these American Indians, many of whom were born naturalists, that its impact can be felt in all the Spanish literature concerning the first decades of the conquest of America. In 1568 Monardes, a physician in Seville, had written a book describing the medicinal plants which came from America, and by 1588 the first natural history of the New World had appeared, written by the Jesuit Father Acosta. In fact there is hardly a document of the time, whether written by a soldier, a missionary, or a merchant, which does not contain some description of curative plants or an account of extraordinary cures performed by the Indians. Thus it has been stated that during the conquest of Peru the soldiers of Pizarro preferred to be treated for their ailments and wounds by the Indians rather than by their Spanish compatriots, which is not surprising, remembering the European remedies of human skull, ground Egyptian mummy, and the like. This proficiency with drugs seems, moreover, to have had special recognition within the system of labor distribution prevailing in the Inca Empire, because Father Calancha, in the same book in which he described the fever tree, explained that in Peru the "study of plants was greatly enhanced by the law which purposely forbade idleness, and stated that those who were physically unfit for war or agriculture should devote themselves to the study of medicinal herbs in order to help the sick. Therefore, there was an infinite number occupied in the classification of curative plants."

The arrival in Europe of all these medicinal plants together with the tales concerning the ability of the Indians in matters of medicine was the reason for the sudden appearance in the Old World of an interest in the study of natural history. Up to the time of the discovery of America all the literature dealing with botany and medicinal plants had referred exclusively to the works of Aristotle, Pliny, and Dioscorides and dwelt only on the plants described by these authors, the most modern of whom had lived in the first century A.D. In the sixteenth century new plants were described, and the first botanical gardens were started. From then on the medical sciences, which had protected themselves so sternly from the renovating influences of the Renaissance, blossomed forth, somewhat slowly and painfully at first but with evident clarity as to the intended goal. By the seventeenth century several natural histories of America had been written and the wonders of the New World became a subject of general curiosity and interest; one of the results of this interest was the uncomfortable fashion of exotic pet animals, cockatoos, parrots, monkeys, and the like being adopted by the elite of the courts.

As for the marvelous bark of the fever tree, in spite of the reputation enjoyed by the Peruvian curative plants, no immediate attempt seems to have been made to take it to Europe. What is more remarkable, however, is the fact that no proof has been found that the new remedy made any sensation in Lima itself where, according to the Augustinian monk, it was producing miraculous results. There is no evidence, for instance, that any attempt was made to give it to the Viceroy Chinchón, in spite of the fact that it was well known in the city that he suffered from a particularly bad tertian fever. The viceroy, moreover, was not only badly in need of the drug but he was also mindful of anything pertaining to the problems of public health. Shortly after taking over his post, he made channel improvements in the Rimac River which periodically flooded whole districts of Lima and thus added to the continual increase of malaria in the city. The viceroy, of course, never suspected that in his flood-control measures he would reduce the incidence of malaria, but it is curious to note that this was the first result of his interest in the welfare of Lima.

He instituted what were probably the first quarantine measures in this hemisphere. As a result of certain epidemics which had been carried into Lima by the arrival of large groups of Negro slaves, he ordered that each Negro should be examined by three physicians before entering the city. The sick ones, moreover, were properly attended to in an isolated building before beginning what was usually a terrible life, which the viceroy had tried to mitigate by attempting, without result, to give the Negro slaves some sort of legal protection. After many difficulties he succeeded in naming two professors of medicine in the University of San Marcos, where these two chairs had been instituted long ago but had never been filled for lack of funds, one of the obstacles in the way of getting funds being that the natives knew the many medicinal plants of the country better than the physicians. On April 17, 1635, Dr. Juan de Vega, private physician to the viceroy, gave what was probably the first lesson in medicine on the American continent, a great event which was solemnly attended by the viceroy, the clergy, and the council of the Crown. By the expressed desire of the viceroy orders had been given that any freak of nature should be taken to his palace. Such extraordinary things as a carrot shaped like a man were therefore presented to him, as well as a giant whose portrait was painted to be preserved as an anatomical document. All these activities of the viceroy seem to suggest that if his attention had been called to the extraordinary bark of the fever tree he would certainly have interested himself in the subject.

The new remedy, however, seems to have sunk into complete oblivion until eleven years after Father Calancha's book was published, that is until 1650 when the bark made a rather startling appearance on the Continent and through the offices of an extraordinary man was thrown into the sedate bosom of the European medical profession with the impact of an incendiary bomb. In the ensuing explosion, which manifested itself as one of the most violent medical controversies in history and took on the proportions of an international scandal because of the high station of the contending parties, the foundations of ancient medicine were disrupted beyond repair. And in the course of the commotion the Count of Chinchón was raised to sudden and unexpected prominence because, as stated by Sebastian Bado, one of the physicians involved in the affair, there was evidence that he had been the first to bring to Europe a large shipment of the bark. He had, moreover, distributed the drug freely to the poor on his arrival in Madrid and sixteen years after his death a great supply of the bark could still be found in his castle of Chinchón, although at all times he had placed it at the disposal of any physician who wanted to experiment on its curative virtues. Bado, who was a physician living in Genoa, also had a story to tell of the curious (and so far unreported) means by which the bark had been conveyed to the attention of the viceroy. The narrative ran as follows:

In the City of Lima, which is the Capital of Peru, the wife of the Viceroy, at that time the Count of Chinchón, fell sick. Her illness was the tertian fever, which in that part is by no means mild but severe and dangerous. The rumor of this illness (as generally happens to important people), which at once became known throughout the city, spread to the neighboring places and reached Loxa.

A Spaniard, who then held the governorship in that place, was informed about the illness of the Countess, and decided to advise her husband the Viceroy by letter. He did so and wrote that he possessed a certain remedy, which he unreservedly recommended, and if the Viceroy would use it, his wife would recover and be free from all fevers. The husband told his wife about this communication and she immediately agreed. Then, since we readily trust that which we hope will profit us, the Viceroy ordered the man from whom he hoped for help to be summoned without delay, and he was therefore ordered to come to Lima at once, which he did. When admitted into the presence of the Viceroy he confirmed verbally what he had said in the letter, and told the Vicereine to be cheerful and confident, since he was certain she would recover if she would stand by his advice. Having heard this she decided to take the remedy, and after taking it, to the amazement of all, she recovered sooner than you can say it.

When this was learned in the City, the people approached the Vicereine by intermediaries, not so much joyfully and congratulatorily but supplicatingly, begging her to deign to help them, and say, if she would, by what remedy she had at last so marvelously, so quickly, recovered, so that they, who often suffered from precisely this fever could also provide for themselves.

The Countess at once agreed. She not only told them what the remedy was, but ordered a large quantity of it to be sent to her to relieve the suffering of the citizens who often suffered from the disease. Not only did she order this great remedy the bark to be brought, but she wished to dispense it to the many sick with her own hands. And the thing turned out so well that, just as she herself had experienced the generous hands of God in that miraculous remedy, so all the needy who took it marvelously recovered their health. And this bark was afterwards called the Countess' Powder, which in Spanish is *los Polvos de la Condesa.*[1]

This charming story was accepted for three hundred years as the official version of the discovery of quinine. A hundred years after the death of the Countess of Chinchón, as a memorial to her philanthropic gesture, the fever tree was officially named the cinchona tree. Lately, however, it has become clear that no corroborative historical evidence could be found to support the story, either of the countess's cure or of her having distributed the bark among the citizens of Lima. How the Count of Chinchón happened to learn about the bark or who brought it to him therefore is not known and in all probability will never be known. That he took the bark to Europe, however, seems to be an established fact. It has been authoritatively affirmed that it was not until a year after his return to Spain that the first written mention of quinine appeared in a medical text and two hundred years after his death traditions were still alive, in the surrounding territories of Chinchón, of miraculous cures brought about by some extraordi-

---

[1] A. W. Haggis, "Fundamental Errors in the Early History of Cinchona," *Bulletin of the History of Medicine,* 1941, Vol. 10, pp. 417-59, 568-92. Reprinted by permission.

nary remedy in the possession of the lords of the castle. Absence of any mention of the drug in the papers of the Count of Chinchón may be attributed to the fact that he himself had given very little importance to this minor enterprise of his. Obsessed as he was by the great reforms he was trying to bring about in the administration of the "Realms of Peru," he overlooked, by one of the frequent ironies of fate, the fact that he had in his hands the means for improving the lives of an untold number of individuals all over the earth.

Unfortunately no one has seen the report about Peru that he wrote for the king in the last years of his life, in which he apparently dealt at length with the natural resources of the country. Yet he was a statesman, not a scientist. After having brought the bark for the physicians to try, his mission was ended. If the medical profession chose to ignore the new remedy, he must have assumed that they knew best, and the bark was probably forgotten in some attic of the castle of Chinchón. That he could not have been very successful in his attempt to introduce the new drug into medicine was no wonder. It took men of far more combativeness, daring, and cunning than was ever possessed by the noble Count of Chinchón to get the bark out of the attic and to force the medical profession to the realization of its existence.

Yet seldom has poetic justice manifested itself in a more appealing form than by inscribing forever, in the exclusive list of the great benefactors of mankind, the name of the man who, born amongst the great, had felt so deeply the sorrows of those born to be the forgotten ones, the Indians of Peru, who through their simple knowledge of the ways of nature had contributed to the world a drug which proved to be without equal in the annals of the history of medicine.

CHAPTER III

The Jesuits' Powder

On December 14, 1643, the consistory of cardinals was in session, presided over by Pope Urban VIII, who made the official announcement that a new cardinal was to be created, a man who, according to His Holiness, was a great defender of the Church, not with the arms of battle but with the weapon of his pen. His name was John de Lugo, a Spaniard and a Jesuit. This was an extraordinary decision on the part of the pontiff. The members of the Society of Jesus were bound by a special vow not to accept external honors, and thus could not hold any position of authority in the hierarchy of the Church; as for the man's nationality, by the seventeenth century the election of Italian popes was already a tacitly established custom—and a cardinal always had a fair chance of becoming pope. Moreover Urban VIII's policies had consistently favored the interests of France with little regard for those of Spain, and a Spanish cardinal was always a potential advocate of the interests of his country.

Although Father de Lugo had been living in Rome for twenty-two years, very few people in the Vatican knew him. He was a teacher of philosophy in the Gregorian University of the Collegio Romano, leading a life of complete retirement, concerned solely with his devotions and his pupils. In spite of the fact that he was a prolific writer, he had published little, and always at the express command of his superiors; yet his pupils had made him famous in the academic world and requests for copies of his lectures were constantly coming from the different European universities.

Urban VIII, on the other hand, was an energetic man very much involved in the political events of the time, and it was hard to imagine what task he had in mind for a philosopher in his council. But Urban VIII knew.

John de Lugo, who had been born in Madrid of a noble and wealthy Spanish family, after spending his childhood in Seville had gone at the age of sixteen to the University of Salamanca to study law and jurisprudence. While continuing his studies he became, a year later, a novice in the Society of Jesus, following the example of his very dear older brother who had also become a Jesuit. At the age of twenty John de Lugo wrote a legal treatise entitled *De Justitia et Jure*. In this treatise, which dealt with the practical aspects of the administration of justice, the author revealed himself as a determined disputant, contradicting precedent, pointing out error, and stating his own and original conclusions with a clarity of exposition and a self-reliance quite amazing for so young a legislator.

The treatise, which became a landmark in the history of law, had an enthusiastic reception and the doors of success were opened wide to its capable author. John de Lugo was still only a novice in the Society of Jesus and could leave it if he so desired; the temptations of worldly achievements must have been very strong for a young man with a powerful intellect, and John de Lugo could not have been unmoved by their irresistible attraction. But he also must have had visions, as folks did in those days, of the devil, dressed up in the gown of a magistrate and surrounded by bags of gold, holding in one hand the scepter, emblem of power, and in the other the scales of justice, while with a wink he smiled enticingly upon the man of God. It was in the name of human justice that the powers of darkness tempted man into committing the grossest violations of the rights of others, with gold and power as his reward. John de Lugo must have become worried about the salvation of his soul, for he suddenly left the field of law and turned to theology. His father remonstrated, pleading with him that because of his ability in practical matters he owed himself to the world. John's decision was unmovable: religion was to him the absolute truth. He was to become a Jesuit and a teacher of philosophy. The law, which served man in his material struggles, was forgotten forever.

Father John de Lugo taught philosophy in Spanish universities and proved to be an eminent theologian. His reputation spread, and when he was thirty-seven years old the Father General of the Society of Jesus decided that he should go to Rome to teach in the Gregorian University. In the year 1643 he had reached the age of sixty; his health, which had always been poor, was now terribly undermined by the inevitable Roman fevers. He must have felt that after an austere and uneventful life the end was near.

But in 1642, *De Justitia et Jure*, written forty years before, had fallen into the hands of the pope, who was amazed by this brilliant display of legal knowledge. Europe was in a turmoil, with the Thirty Years' War raging at its height, and the papacy was trying hard to find a way of stopping this conflict while at the same time it was engaged in the endless disputes that had resulted from the Reformation. Men like De Lugo, with clear, practical minds, were badly needed in the Vatican.

Once in the presence of the pontiff, who was to invest the future cardinal with the attributes of his rank, John de Lugo stated that in accordance with the vow he had made, which forbade him the acceptance of external honors, he was compelled to refuse the dignity offered him. Urban VIII reminded him that by his authority he could give him a special dispensation; therefore he was free to break his vow. Father de Lugo had not taught philosophy in vain: "If I am free, how can I by my own volition break a pledge to which I am indissolubly bound?" Only one course was left to the pope: Father John de Lugo was to become a cardinal by express precept of obedience.

John de Lugo had to submit; but after his investiture, the first and last ceremony he ever attended in the papal court, Cardinal de Lugo returned to his former way of life. He used only a few of the rooms in the palace given to him, and he reduced to a minimum the number of servants, never allowing anyone to attend to his personal needs. His income as cardinal was spent in charities because Cardinal de Lugo, like St. Paul, praised charity above all other virtues.

Whether Cardinal de Lugo fulfilled the expectation of the pope is not known. The pope himself did not have much chance to decide because he died seven months later, in July 1644. To elect the new pope it was necessary to hold a conclave, at which the presence of the foreign cardinals was required; but the summer fevers were raging throughout the city of Rome. Furthermore traveling through the Roman Campagna during that time of the year was sheer suicide. The terrible happenings during the preceding conclave, when Urban VIII had been elected, were still fresh in the minds of everyone: eight cardinals and thirty attendants, who had come to the conclave as clerks and secretaries, had died. Urban VIII, immediately after the election, had left the Vatican in haste and had moved his court to the Quirinal; it was easy enough to contract the fevers anywhere in Rome but in the Vatican, which was located in a particularly unhealthy spot, they were unavoidable.

The present situation was a similar one and the physicians forbade the celebration of the conclave until autumn. France was most eager that this resolution should be carried out because Guido Cardinal Bentivoglio, who at that precise moment was in the French court as papal nuncio, was the very man whom everybody there expected to succeed Urban VIII and to continue his pro-French policy. Fevers or no fevers, if the conclave was held Cardinal Bentivoglio would have to go to Rome to be elected pope. Urban VIII, whose name was Maffeo Barberini, had made two of his nephews cardinals and they had been most influential during their uncle's reign. The Cardinals Barberini decided on a bold stroke: the conclave was to be celebrated against the advice of the physicians and the new pope would have to be elected by the votes of the cardinals residing in Rome, who up to that moment had been most compliant to the interests of the House of Barberini, hence to the interests of France. Cardinal Bentivoglio rushed to Rome, crossed the Roman Campagna, and got there in time for the opening of the conclave which took place on August ninth.

Cardinal de Lugo was on his way to the conclave when he was stopped at the door by the two Cardinals Barberini. "Your Eminence will not forget that the House of Barberini made you cardinal," he was told. To which he answered, "Three obligations I am under, which I want very much to fulfill. The first is to God, who has redeemed me, the second to my country, which made me the man I am, and the third to the House of Barberini, which has bestowed honors upon me. If the interests of the latter are not opposed to the interests of the first two I shall do my best to remember my obligation to the House of Barberini." And with this he swept past the door into the room.

Three weeks after the conclave started, Guido Cardinal Bentivoglio died of the Roman fevers; France had lost an ally and the Barberinis a protector. Cardinal Pamphili was elected pope and took the name of Innocent X. Cardinal de Lugo's first two obligations, to his God and to his country, were thus well served by the fevers of Rome that had eliminated Cardinal Bentivoglio, for Innocent X was a devout servant of God and a great ally of Spain. However, the realization of the way this relentless nightmare had turned the most important proceeding of the Church into a weird and haunted assemblage left an everlasting impression on De Lugo's mind. He himself, together with other cardinals, had been very ill at the time and he had probably become reinfected during his stay in the Vatican, where of necessity he had to remain during the conclave.

Great as may have been Cardinal de Lugo's influence on the papacy, it was always kept in the background. Historians do not mention him; in the political imbroglios of the seventeenth century he is a non-existent figure. Yet in spite of his efforts to the contrary, he became one of the most discussed men of his time, though one quite forgotten by posterity.

In 1649, five years after the election of Innocent X, the Father General of the Society of Jesus died and the provincial fathers from all over the world congregated in Rome to elect a new Father General. Needless to say Cardinal de Lugo played a most important role in such a gathering, and it appears that in this congregation of Jesuit fathers a subject was discussed which had nothing to do with religious matters. The subject was the Peruvian bark, the remedy from the New World which supposedly cured the "fevers" and which so far had failed to attract much attention from the medical profession. A few physicians seem to have tried it, but as yet no one had bothered to make a careful study of its medicinal properties.

With the expansion of the Spanish Empire the Society of Jesus had become mainly concerned with the problem of missions, and the missionary fathers were constantly confronted with sanitary problems whose solution would be most helpful in their task of saving souls. On the other hand, having lived for years among the so-called primitive people in the most inaccessible spots of the globe, the missionaries had had a chance to observe the resourcefulness with which man managed to survive in the most adverse conditions. They themselves had been treated many a time in their ailments by the ministrations of medicine men; strange brews had been given to them, thoroughly innocuous most of the time but now and then amazingly effective. Thus they had become both openminded and curious, two qualities sadly lacking in the scientific world of their day, and they were willing to put to the test empirical suggestions that the scholastic mind rejected as pure nonsense. Hence it was no wonder that this purely religious organization should concern itself with a problem of therapeutics that the medical profession had chosen to ignore.

The Jesuits, who through their missions in Peru had easy access to the bark, had in all probability given it freely to people stricken by the ague and had good reason to believe in the effectiveness of the remedy. Still, as long as the physicians refused to use it, there was no question of its introduction into medicine. The Peruvian bark needed a sponsor, and in the hope of finding one the provincial father from Peru had taken a considerable amount of the remedy to Rome.

That the situation should have been presented to Cardinal de Lugo by his Jesuit brethren seems a logical conclusion, but that Cardinal de Lugo should have done anything about it seems a far less logical one. He had been a sick man all his life; he had an idiosyncrasy rather common to people with poor health: namely, an intense dislike for medical topics or anything related to medicine. Moreover, the problem of sponsoring a remedy disregarded by the medical profession presented implications which, for a man who had spent his whole life in the realms of metaphysical speculation, should have been of a terrifying nature.

But within the theologian was the man who, forty-five years before, had written a legal treatise in which he had shown a superb command of the situation when arguing and contradicting on behalf of man's temporal rights. This man, who rejoiced in earthly controversy, had been put to sleep because he was a threat to the spiritual peace of a mystic, and yet in the life of Cardinal de Lugo there was a very deep, dark secret. In the midst of his teachings, theological writings, devotions, and charities the temptation of profane learning persistently clouded the purity of his yearnings. Apparently Cardinal de Lugo had weakened, and in great mystery he had conducted some experiments for the purpose of solving certain problems relating to mathematics and physics. From his experiments he succeeded in formulating a law which, in spite of his secrecy, eventually became known as his own. According to this law, called "of inflation points," some substances in certain conditions could fill more or less space without increasing or diminishing in quantity; this principle, experimentally proved later on by the scientist Robert Boyle, became one of the fundamental laws of modern chemistry.

Cardinal de Lugo therefore had in him not only the spirit of a fighter but also the analytical power of a scientist. That no one had felt the urge to experiment with the new remedy if for no other reason than sheer curiosity sounded to him like monstrous stupidity. The new remedy, moreover, came from the New World, toward which De Lugo's eyes were constantly turned, for out there his beloved Jesuit brother was teaching in the great University of Mexico, where he discoursed in faultless Latin to Aztec princes of the blood on the mysteries of sacred theology. It may be that all his life the cardinal had longed for the New World ever since as a child he had watched in Seville the arrival of the Spanish galleons from the Indies, loaded with gold and silver as well as plants of every description: strange herbs and roots and aromatic resins and balsams and seeds and spices and fruits, all endowed with medicinal virtues. Monardes, the physician from Seville, had called these marvels of nature "The joyfull newes out of the New-found worlde." With the galleons also came tales, fantastic tales, of endless forests of gigantic trees, the tops of which man could not see; of rivers so wide that man could not perceive one side from the other; of colossal mountains which were constantly being moved by roaring earthquakes; of snakes so long and powerful that they could kill a bull by twirling themselves around it; of eagles so enormous in size that they could fly away with a llama; of birds that could talk; of monkeys that looked like men. The medical profession had never seen this fabulous New World, from which anything might come—even a drug that could free man from the accursed fevers which kept him shivering and shaking in eternal agony.

Now, for the first time, John de Lugo was confronted with a challenge which he could not ignore without accusing himself of cowardice. He had refused to help man in the struggle for his material possessions in order to help him in the more important struggle to save his soul. Could he also refuse to try to save millions of people from a disease which not only afflicted them with the evils of physical pain but which also dragged them to the depths of untold misery and poverty? John de Lugo, who was past the mystical ardors of youth, knew quite well that illness and poverty are great obstacles on the road to perfection. The fighter, who for so long had been held in subjection, had finally encountered a cause worthy of his combative power and, forgetting that he was now a decrepit old cardinal, John de Lugo took up the challenge.

After having discussed the matter with Innocent X, who gave him complete freedom of action, Cardinal de Lugo requested that the pope's physician carry out a careful study of the medicinal properties of the Peruvian bark. This physician, Fonseca, who was also a Spaniard, performed the task to the best of his ability. His decision was to the effect that not only had he failed to detect any harmful properties in the bark but that it was a most effective remedy in the treatment of fevers. This decision, which showed that Fonseca was a man who could trust his own judgment without getting entangled with prevailing medical theories, was most important from the official point of view. The pope's physician was the supreme

authority in medicine in the Catholic world, and it was for-
tunate for the world at large that on this occasion he was
worthy of the authority conferred upon him.

From now on, as far as De Lugo was concerned, the medical
profession was wrong. The Peruvian bark was a priceless
remedy that must be made known at all costs. Cardinal de
Lugo had great quantities of the bark sent to him and on his
own responsibility had it distributed free in his palace and
also in the pharmacy of the Collegio Romano. In the year
1650 the Peruvian bark was already a popular remedy in
Rome and, the good news having spread abroad, streams of
pilgrims flowed to the Eternal City to take home some of
the new medicine. Cardinal de Lugo was also an eloquent
preacher, and the pilgrims thronged the church to hear and
see the man responsible for such a precious gift. It must have
been through these people that the bark became known as
the "Powder of the Most Eminent Cardinal de Lugo." Meanwhile the Society of Jesus undertook to have the bark exported
from Peru; the Jesuit fathers, wherever they were, became
the promoters of the remedy and thus it was also known as
the "Jesuits' powder" or the "Jesuits' bark."

Innocent X had given his blessing to the enterprise and the
Church, with De Lugo as its leader, found itself plunged in
a campaign to fight the prejudice against the drug. In 1651
there was published in Rome the *Schedula Romana*, a
booklet issued by the Jesuits and signed by several prominent
Roman physicians, in which instructions were given as to the
best way of administering the bark. The medical profession,
regardless of their opinion of the drug, kept silent and Catholic
physicians at least were not in a position to oppose a remedy
openly sponsored by the Church itself.

The bark, thus promoted, was quickly becoming a medicine common to the general practitioner, and it began to find its way into the royal palaces. In the autumn of 1652 it was administered, following the instructions of the *Schedula Romana,* to the Archduke Leopold of Austria, governor of the Low Countries, who had a double quartan fever. The archduke's own physician, Joan Jacob Chiflet, had sponsored the experiment and the archduke had been cured; but a month later the fever returned.

This unfortunate relapse was a common occurrence, since no one knew the proper way of administering the bark. The *Schedula Romana* was a hastily written manual. The medical profession as a matter of principle would not condescend to study the action of a drug which it ignored and consequently the remedy was left in the hands of the layman. This was a source of great confusion as to the curative virtues of the bark, as was also the fact that it was given for all kinds of fevers when it was a specific remedy for the ague and nothing else. Hence a physician who lived in a non-malarious district and had given the bark to patients with typhoid fever could proclaim with good reason that the bark was a worthless medicine. That the fever he was dealing with was of a different kind from the one the bark could cure was not known to him, since up to the seventeenth century and long afterward diseases were classified by symptoms and not by causes, a logical procedure since the causes were unknown. Therefore any disease that produced fever, whether it was pneumonia, a sore throat, the ague, or the plague, was supposed to be caused by the same agency. Though some people were killed by the fever in a few days while others continued to have periodic attacks for years and still others died after weeks of a continuous temperature, it was thought to be the identical process modified by constitutional differences in the patients. So today, if twenty individuals have typhoid fever, no one doubts that they have the identical disease though ten may die and the other ten survive.

In the particular case of the Archduke Leopold of Austria, the administration of the Peruvian bark had been most appropriate since he suffered from a quartan fever. When a month later he had another attack he should have been given more of the remedy. But this august prince felt himself outraged because the bark had not delivered him at once of his malady and decided to show his royal displeasure by denouncing the new remedy as a fraud. Consequently he ordered that his physician, in defiance of the Vatican, should write a book warning mankind against the use of this fallacious medicine.

The book, called *Exposure of the Febrifuge Powder from the American World*, by Joan Jacob Chiflet, "First Physician of the Royal Archduke," appeared in 1653 and was received in the medical world with a great cry of relief. Finally someone had come to deliver the helpless sick from the pestilence with which they were threatened. Chiflet insisted that no one in Brussels had been permanently cured by the bark and that, moreover, according to complaints from Florence, Naples, Madrid, Paris, and Vienna, the drug was a dangerous substance. He maintained that the attacks of fever were caused by the fermentation of a particular "principle," most harmful to the organism, which had to be destroyed or, better still, expelled from the body obviously by purging, bleeding, and emetics—not a very original theory since Galen had expounded it seventeen hundred years before. Again following Galen's system of classifying substances by their taste and according to which anything bitter was dry, he concluded that the bark, which was as bitter as it could be, would dry out the inside of the patient and thus burn out the intestines. When it came to giving proof of the uselessness and harmfulness of the remedy, he referred exclusively to the case of the archduke, apparently the only person to whom he had ever administered the drug. Obviously the high station of his patient could compensate for the limited range of his experience. A royal archduke being worth probably twenty commoners, it was as if the drug had failed in twenty cases of quartan fever.

Chiflet's book was the signal for the rebellion; the medical profession was no longer afraid of the Vatican, Chiflet was hailed by his brethren as the savior of mankind, and his book was reprinted several times.

But neither was Cardinal de Lugo afraid of the medical profession and a prompt reply to Chiflet was published in Rome in the form of a book called *Vindication of the Peruvian Powder*, in which the author maintained that in the same year 1653 thousands of people in Rome had been cured of the fevers by this remedy. The book was signed with the name of Antimus Conygius, which appeared to be the pseudonym of a French Jesuit, Honoré Fabri, who in the course of time became famous for his ability to appropriate to himself other people's discoveries. Nonetheless he was brilliant and most learned and thus has been described as "a universal scholar, a living encyclopedia who delighted in the definition of things of a rather obscure and doubtful nature, being also addicted to the proposition of systems as confusing as they were useless." It must have been that, dazzled by such limitless erudition, the cardinal chose him as the crusader to fight for the new remedy; or it may have been because of the sad fact that no physician had been willing to undertake the task. Whatever the reason for the cardinal's choice, it proved to be most unfortunate. Fabri's qualities, which undoubtedly made of him a very stimulating opponent, also made him a very weak one. Unable to restrain his love for the proposition of systems "as confusing as they were useless," instead of confining himself to the results obtained by experience in the administration of the bark, he indulged quite injudiciously in medical speculations which clearly showed that he was no physician. This together with the fact that a strong suspicion prevailed at the time that Antimus Conygius was De Lugo himself proved to be fatal to the cause of the Peruvian bark.

The Archduke Leopold of Austria was no one to fear cardinals either. His wrath was now fully aroused and, luckier than De Lugo, he found a really capable champion for his cause in an illustrious and powerful member of the medical profession who bore the formidable name of Vopiscus Fortunatus Plempius and the more formidable title of "Rector Magnificus of the University of Louvain," where he was professor of medicine. To his name and title Professor Plempius joined a bellicose disposition and a reputation for "revelling in all the important controversies of the time"; for this pursuit he was endowed with much book learning and a thundering and poisonous eloquence which confounded his opponents regardless of who was right or wrong. No better person to reduce to cinders Fabri's medical gibberings in favor of the Peruvian bark could have been found. The archduke therefore asked Professor Plempius to write a book in answer to Conygius; Plempius complied with great zest and the firm intention of stopping, once and forever, the impudent and unwarranted meddlings in medical matters of men who should be more discreet than to interfere in problems quite outside their province. In his book he first maintained that he had not understood a word of Conygius's arguments, which was probably true; that, however, did not bother him because he insisted on the fact that he did not have the least desire to understand them. He understood well enough the writings of Hippocrates, Galen, and Avicenna, who knew how to write about medicine and who had never spoken of powders as remedies, let alone powders from Peru. How Hippocrates could have heard of a powder from Peru, having lived seventeen centuries before Columbus, Plempius did not explain. As for the fact that Cardinal de Lugo was openly sponsoring the new remedy, he refused to believe it, since this eminent man was known to him as a great theologian but in no other capacity, medical or otherwise. Plempius's book was in fact a malicious and spiteful tirade full of prejudice, abounding in disparaging remarks against the drug and against everything and everybody connected with it. Of scientific impartiality there was none. He quoted three cases in which the drug had failed. He maintained most emphatically that the administration of the bark had the effect of turning sporadic attacks of fever into daily fever. This was an astonishing statement which showed that he himself could not possibly have had any experience with the drug he was so fiercely denouncing. In his frenzy to disgrace the bark he seemed to have lost all sense of decorum for, having quoted a letter from the physician of the King of Spain discrediting the drug, he was publicly accused later on of having forged it.

Yet Dr. Plempius was to all appearances a man both intelligent and honorable. He had always been fond of displaying his controversial powers, and years before, when Harvey published his discovery of the circulation of the blood, Plempius had vilified him for daring to contradict the ancients. To annihilate his antagonist he had repeated Harvey's experiments, only to realize, with sorrow no doubt, that Harvey was right, and Plempius publicly apologized to him for his previous attacks. This noble behavior made his uncompromising and dubious attitude concerning the Peruvian bark still more mystifying. Strangely enough, the explanation can perhaps be found in an old theological controversy, which has given no end of concern to the fathers of the Church, regarding "predestination" as opposed to "free will": whether all men can attain grace as a recompense to be achieved by human effort or whether grace is granted only to the elect and thus is denied to the rest no matter how hard they may try to attain it.

The Jesuits had all along been the defenders of free will; in their missionary zeal they were most eager that this liberal point of view should prevail in the Church so that the heathen could clearly understand that the doors of heaven were wide open to him if only he wanted to make the necessary effort to reach them. About 1640 a book by a priest named Jansen, who was a teacher at the University of Louvain, was published which apparently upheld the theory of predestination, and in the middle of the century the issue was revived with such violence that it nearly tore Europe apart, with the Jansenists on one side and the Jesuits on the other.

Cardinal de Lugo was the first to attack Jansenism; anything that could convey the idea of denying to any man the hope of redemption, were he the most abject human being, was repugnant to his charitable nature. He pleaded that the Church should "increase to an abundant and accessible rain the meager brook of repentance"; he ardently believed in the infinite mercy of God toward His children, the sinner and the righteous alike.

Innocent X declared that certain propositions in Jansen's book were heretical and the Jansenists were branded as heretics. It is very likely that Cardinal de Lugo played an important part in bringing about this decision of the pontiff.

During the heat of the controversy the University of Louvain had become the bulwark of Jansenism. That a professor of Louvain, who was a contemporary of Jansen, should oppose with such blind fury a remedy sponsored by an anti-Jansenist Jesuit gives rise to the suspicion that the bark was not the real issue. Plempius, moreover, who was born in Amsterdam, had been a Protestant until the age of thirty-two, when he embraced the Catholic faith, not because of newly acquired convictions but in order to accept the position of professor of medicine at the University of Louvain, at the time under the authority of the Spanish Crown. Being therefore a Protestant at heart, Plempius naturally felt the greatest dislike for the theological subtilities of the Jesuits and an overwhelming leaning toward the theory of predestination. But the result of all these theological disquisitions was that the fever-stricken people, whether Catholic, Protestant, Mohammedan, or Buddhist, were the ones to suffer. Plempius was a power and a great leader in the medical world and his devastating attack upon the bark resulted in its final banishment from every country but the papal territories where Cardinal de Lugo, indifferent to all menacing protests, continued giving it away to all who wanted it.

Furthermore in 1655, the year in which Plempius's book appeared, a deadly epidemic of the plague ravaged the city of

Rome. Cardinal de Lugo, now seventy-two years old, performed heroic deeds running through the streets, tending
personally to the sick, and giving spiritual comfort to the
dying. In reward for his assistance the city of Rome made him
a member of the Board of Public Health. The enemies of the
Peruvian bark pointed out that now was a good chance to
prove the virtues of his precious remedy. But the celebrated
"Powder of the Most Eminent Cardinal de Lugo" proved to
be absolutely worthless against this terrible disease. How could
any right-thinking man contend against so definite an argument? And the medical profession rejoiced in its glory.

Still, in this same year, an event took place which should
have been of the greatest significance in the eyes of physicians
had they not been blinded by prejudice. Innocent X died and
for the first time in the history of the papacy there was held
in Rome a conclave at which the fevers were not a problem;
no deaths occurred and no illness was recorded.

Yet to all appearances Cardinal de Lugo had lost his fight,
although the controversy about the drug still dragged on for
a time after his death. Three men, the only ones out of the
whole medical world, a Dr. Bado, a Dr. Sturm, and a Dr.
Brunacios, published books in favor of the bark, contradicting
Plempius and Chiflet. Dr. Sturm, who was a compatriot of
Plempius practicing in Delft, vehemently insisted on the fact
that the Peruvian bark had a specific curative virtue for the
ague, that in the light of prevailing medical theories it could
not be explained why this should be so but that the facts were
true, and that anyone who refused to consider these facts acted
either out of ignorance or out of bad faith, the latter being
the more probable in view of the futility of the arguments put
forward against the effectiveness of the bark. Chiflet and

Plempius together could not quote more than four cases in which the drug had failed while he, Sturm, could quote not less than seventeen cases in which a complete cure had taken place. That a man as competent as Plempius should say anything so ludicrous as that the bark turned the ague into a daily fever could be attributed not to ignorance but to sheer malevolence.

The last book defending the Peruvian bark appeared in 1663 and from then on many years were to pass before another word was written in its behalf. Popular prejudice finally sided with the medical profession against the drug, and the Jesuits very likely desisted from bringing the bark in large quantities from Peru due to the risks involved in the enterprise once the drug had been branded as dangerous. Only a year after De Lugo's death a physician in Copenhagen was presented with three doses of the Jesuits' powder by some friends who had been traveling in Italy and who had brought it home as a rarity. The physician, out of curiosity, gave them to a patient with a double quartan fever and the results were so amazing that he tried desperately to get more of the remedy; but the Jesuits' powder could not be had. When the bark lost its sponsor the fate of the people suffering from the ague no longer concerned anyone.

Cardinal de Lugo died in the year 1660, a tired old man of seventy-seven who had spent the last ten years of his life in a humiliating and seemingly fruitless struggle. At his request he was buried at the foot of Ignatius Loyola's tomb, with an inscription stating that there lies "John Cardinal de Lugo, a most eminent theologian of the Society of Jesus." Of his fight on behalf of a drug which was going to become one of man's priceless possessions, not a word. That is probably the way he wanted it, to be remembered only as the servant of God; and as such, a hundred years later, Benedict XIV said of him that he was a "luminary of the Church," a great Christian philosopher second only to Thomas Aquinas. At least the Church had a kind word for him while the medical world, after scorning and vilifying him, consistently ignored the man who had tried so hard to put into its hands what proved to be one of medicine's most valuable weapons.

Yet Cardinal de Lugo was amply avenged; the medical profession was to learn its lesson, and a bitter one it was to be, because the man who picked up the fight where he had left it was no bearer of noble weapons and it was by covering the medical profession with ridicule that he succeeded in establishing the "Powder of the Most Eminent Cardinal de Lugo."

CHAPTER IV

Philosophical Interlude

*The Idols and false Notions which have already
preoccupied the human Understanding, and are
deeply rooted in it, not only so beset men's Minds,
that they become difficult of access, but even when
access is obtained, will again meet and trouble us in
the instauration of the Sciences, unless mankind,
when forewarned, guard themselves with all possible care against them.*

FRANCIS BACON

Although Cardinal de Lugo's attempt to introduce the
Peruvian bark into medicine had failed, almost every country
in Europe had had a taste of the Jesuits' powder before its
ultimate disgrace. One country, however, had been spared the
experiment: England, where the ague was a national calamity.
In seventeenth-century English such phrases as an "ague of
terror" or "ague of fear" were common figures of speech and
as late as the middle of the nineteenth century Emerson con-
tended that an Englishman's hilarity was like an attack of
fever. The England of 1650, when the bark first appeared in
Rome, was "Puritan England." The year before, King Charles
I had been executed and his Catholic wife with her children
sent into exile. In 1653 Oliver Cromwell became the nation's

Protector and the zealous guardian of the Protestant faith. The general prejudice against the Roman Catholic Church and against the English Catholics themselves was at a high peak. Cromwell in his fervor for the Protestant cause was easily led into the extremes of bigotry; his hatred for the papacy could only be compared to his hatred for Spain, which he considered "the head of the papal interests"; and he went so far as to tell Parliament, "The papists in England have been accounted, ever since I was born, Spaniolized." Thus the Roman Catholics in England were looked upon more as traitors to their country than as religious dissidents. The suspicion of "popery" was easily aroused. In these circumstances it is small wonder that no one would undertake to bring into England a medicine coming from the Spanish colonies, sponsored by the Vatican, and known by the abhorrent name of the Jesuits' powder. The animosity against anything "popish" had saved the English medical profession from the trouble of opposing the new drug; but not for long, however, because destiny had decreed that in England should be sealed once and for all the fate of the new remedy.

The ague, meanwhile, was rampant throughout the nation and London was its favorite site; there were so many marshes in and about the city that Oliver Cromwell was called in derision "the King of the Marshes." In the swamps of London as in those of Greece and Rome, the malignant miasma reigned undisturbed.

In 1658 the ague became epidemic in England and, according to an eyewitness, in the autumn the whole island had the appearance of a public hospital. It was probably due to this situation that in the same year the new remedy made its first appearance in England through the unglorious vehicle of an advertisement, according to which, "the Fever Bark commonly called the Jesuits' Powder, which is so famous for the cure of all manner of Agues," could be had "at the lodgings of Mr. James Thompson, merchant from Antwerp, or at Mr. John Crook's bookseller, with directions for its use." Strangely enough the authenticity of the bark was attested by Dr. Prujean, a physician of great repute and president of the College of Physicians, though he was suspected of being a papist.

Whether it was due to Dr. Prujean's prestige or to sheer desperation at the progress of the epidemic, the fact is that there took place in England that year the first recorded trial of the new drug, which was given to a Mr. Underwood, alderman of the city of London; but Mr. Underwood died. His death was immediately attributed to the Jesuits' powder and since he was a well-known, respected citizen the incident provoked much comment.

Shortly thereafter it became apparent that Oliver Cromwell, the Protector, was dying of the ague. London's great physicians argued in consultation whether the Jesuits' powder ought to be given to the Protector in spite of the recent Underwood episode. Of course anyone too sanguine about the drug might have been suspected of being a papist, and his position, therefore, would have become exceedingly difficult had the administration of this remedy appeared to result in the Protector's death. Consequently, nobody daring to undertake the great experiment, Cromwell died of the ague in his fifty-ninth year when he might have been saved; thus he himself fell victim to the prejudices he had aroused.

Two years later, in 1660, the monarchic restoration took place and Charles II became King of England. One of his first acts was a royal declaration granting freedom of religion with the main purpose of alleviating the plight of the Catholics, since he himself was a Catholic at heart, though such is the fate of kings that he was the only man in England who could not avail himself of the instituted freedom. The sympathy of Charles II for the Catholics, his marriage to a Portuguese Catholic princess, and the fact that his own brother, heir presumptive to the throne, had made a public profession of the Catholic faith, ought to have secured the position of the followers of Rome. Actually it had the opposite effect. The people at large became afraid, and with good reason, that the king might declare himself a Roman Catholic and enforce Catholicism as the state religion. This, to the great majority of the English Protestants, would have meant not only the betrayal of the Protestant faith but the political control of England by the Catholic powers, mainly France and Spain. Thus the old hatred for the Catholics was exacerbated by the need of concealing it in order not to antagonize the court.

The tension resulting from this situation may perhaps explain the silence that shrouded the Jesuits' powder in England during the first years after Charles II's accession to the throne. After the ill-fated trial of the bark on Mr. Underwood, Dr. Thomas Willis mentioned the drug in 1660, the year of the Restoration, saying in effect that it might stop the attack but did not cure the fever; thus it was looked upon as a kind of palliative, something like the aspirin of our day. After that the whole English medical profession seemed to be quite unaware of the existence of a medicine with the uncomfortable name of the Jesuits' powder. If it was used, as it seems to have been, it was taken in a non-specific fashion. The unassuming Dr. Prujean, once the sponsor of the drug, used it in ministering to the queen, who suffered from a very bad tertian fever. He gave her unnamed cordials which had a marvelous effect on her attacks. Yet no one in the court, besides the Catholic queen, seemed to care for the services of popish-suspected Prujean.

Then came the year 1666, when Thomas Sydenham published his memorable *Method for Curing the Fevers*. Sydenham was one of the great physicians of his time and his influence in medicine is comparable to that of Hippocrates or Galen. In fact he was one of the most devoted followers of Hippocrates, believing implicitly in the wisdom of the latter's advice that the function of medicine was to detect the symptoms and signs which made the sick man different from the well man and those that made one sick man different from another sick man. This Sydenham summarized brilliantly by saying that there are no diseases, there are sick people, meaning that although a number of people may suffer from the same ailment each individual reacts differently to its effect. Therefore the physician should always be ready to cope with any surprises since, no matter how well he knows the disease with which he is confronted, in his particular patient it may run a course bearing no resemblance whatsoever to the standard descriptions in the textbook. The obvious implication then was that medicine was not an exact science, to be learned from books, but an art, requiring imagination and the gift of improvisation, to be mastered only by the careful observation of every patient as an independent entity. In the seventeenth century, when physicians went through medical school without so much as seeing a patient with a common cold, Sydenham's conclusions were of a revolutionary nature.

Like every physician since Hippocrates' time, he was obsessed by the disease called "fevers." What were fevers? What caused them? In some cases the "fever" was accompanied by symptoms such as respiratory or intestinal disturbances which could explain why there was a fever. But what drove the physicians to distraction was the other kind, the chemically pure fever. The patient was in perfect health and suddenly, as if hit by lightning, he shuddered, shivered, and had a "fever" —a fever and absolutely nothing else: that is, the malarial fevers.

Hippocrates of Cos had said that the fever was the result of a process of fermentation of the blood by which the corrupt humors, cause of the disease, were destroyed or expelled from the body. And no disease could bear out this statement more thoroughly than malaria. Since at the onset of the disease there was nothing organically wrong with the malarial patient, his humors, which escaped the naked eye, had to be the site of the disease. As for the process of fermentation, the peculiar features of the paroxysm, with the rapid increase in temperature, could amply suggest to the imagination a sudden eruption of the blood to eliminate the poisonous matter, like the overflowing of milk when it reaches its boiling point. On this basis Galen's contention that diseases could be cured only by bleeding and purging in order to help nature in the deliverance of its corrupt humors was unassailable. Malaria then was the Achilles' heel of Galenic medicine; should it ever be proved that malaria could be cured without need of expelling corrupt humors, it would be the end of Galenism. But could such a thing be done? For centuries the most original minds in medicine had pondered the cause of malarial fevers and had had to surrender to Hippocrates' explanations and to Galen's methods of treatment. In the seventeenth century Sydenham too surrendered—needlessly, because he was the first great physician who had been provided with the arrow that could pierce the Galenic heel to the bone. Yet he turned the weapon against himself, in an effort to protect the edifice so carefully built up throughout two thousand years of medical speculation.

In his *Method for Curing the Fevers*, Sydenham cited the Jesuits' powder as proof that the malarial fevers were caused by the corrupt humors: because this powder, which lowered the temperature, stopped the process of fermentation by which the humors were expelled and thus was a great danger to the life of the patient. And he would admit only that *such remedies*, given cautiously and prudently, might have some beneficial effects if administered as the fever declined, that is, after the corrupt humors had been eliminated. Sydenham thus implied that he was afraid to use the new remedy although it was obvious that he had had no experience with it.

Why then did he reach such definite conclusions as to its harmful properties? That Chiflet had done so was not surprising. He was a court physician much too busy keeping up with the duties of a fashionable doctor to bother with experimentations of any kind. When the bark failed to cure the archduke his position may have become seriously threatened because he had allowed his royal master to take what was after all an unknown and practically untested remedy; in his extremity he blamed it on the bark. As for Plempius, though he was a man of great talent, he had become a type well known in the academic world: the sum of all knowledge, the receptacle of limitless wisdom, dogmatic, intolerant, and unbearably pedantic. He knew that the bark was no good without having to spend his valuable time proving it, and no confounded Jesuit was going to tell him the contrary.

Sydenham was different; he really was a man of science. He knew facts when he saw them and he knew how to evaluate them. Why then was the spirit of scientific inquiry so dormant in him that he did not look for the facts concerning the Jesuits' powder? Because Sydenham, who understood so well the wisdom of the ancients, also shared their faults. Following their example, he was an impartial observer of the facts that confronted him, and he recorded them faithfully. But also like them, he had to state the reasons for these facts in a thoroughly dogmatic fashion. Being dogmatic, Sydenham had to be scholastic in his way of reasoning. He had accepted as dogma Hippocrates' proposition that diseases were caused by the corrupt humors. Therefore the new remedy, which was not a purge nor an emetic and in no way expelled fluids from the body, could not cure because it left the corrupt matter within the sick man; *ergo,* it was harmful. This was a perfect example of medieval scholasticism and the irrefutable logic of this conclusion could only be shaken by attacking it at the base: that is, by suggesting that diseases might not be caused by the corrupt humors, which could be proved by showing how the Jesuits' powder cured the malarial fevers. Thus Thomas Sydenham epitomized the reasons for the relentless opposition of the medical profession to the new drug, which could not be overcome because they ran in a vicious circle: there was no need to test the drug because it did not expel humors, and the only way of demonstrating that there were no humors to be expelled was by testing the drug.

Yet no matter how conformist a group or a society may be, it always shelters a number of hopelessly curious men; and curiosity is probably the main incentive for inquiry into the unknown. By 1666 only three men in the European medical world had been curious enough to experiment with the new remedy. But their example had been enough to deter anyone else from following in their footsteps, because these men had shown that in the light of prevailing knowledge the cure of malarial fevers by the bark could not be explained by any possible stretch of the imagination. This acceptance of facts regardless of whether or not they fitted within the framework of preconceived theories and beliefs was sheer empiricism, the complete reverse of the prevailing scholastic system.

The issue was not new in the seventeenth century. In the fields of astronomy and mathematics Copernicus and Galileo had caused revolutionary changes by following the empirical —or rather, the experimental—method, according to which any theory not based on facts was a doubtful proposition until confirmed by those facts. However, in spite of the fact that Sir Francis Bacon had already insisted on the necessity of applying the experimental method to the study of diseases, at the time Thomas Sydenham wrote his *Method for Curing the Fevers* the new philosophy had not yet pervaded the medical world.

Although Vesalius had already written his *Anatomy*, which proved the ancients' ignorance of the human body, and Harvey had made his discovery of the circulation of the blood which also refuted the ancients' explanation of this phenomenon, these two great discoveries had had little effect on the daily practice of medicine. They had been officially repudiated and it is doubtful whether the rank-and-file practitioner knew much about them. But even those who had accepted them could not visualize at the time any incompatability between them and the prevailing explanations of the causes of diseases. Thus the philosopher Descartes, who had become a champion of Harvey's discovery and was also a defender of the experimental method, still believed implicitly in the theory of the humors.

The introduction into medicine of the Peruvian bark, on the other hand, had a direct bearing on the practice of medicine, since it was a remedy for fevers and thus would have to be handled by every practitioner. And it also had a direct bearing on the scholastic system, since medical schools would have to teach its usage without being able to explain its mode of action, a procedure considered worthy only of quacks, who at the time were called empirics.

Consequently Thomas Sydenham, who in all probability was willing enough to substitute one explanation for another, could not turn into an empiric. Thus he carefully avoided the trap laid for him by the Jesuits' powder, quite unconscious of the great harm he was doing to his fellow men. Being the greatest physician of his time, it fell upon him to decide for or against the new remedy in a manner worthy of his ability, not by merely quoting other people's unwarranted conclusions. Yet he was the depository of an old heritage where the wrong and the right were intermingled. Afraid that the destruction of one part might bring about the collapse of the whole, in an effort to protect what was wise in the old doctrines he disregarded the new facts.

Two years later, in 1668, a second edition of the *Method for Curing the Fevers* was published. The paragraphs dealing with the Jesuits' powder were a transcription of the first edition. Sydenham had nothing to correct, nothing to add to his former conclusions.

Again it was the turn of the fever-stricken people to suffer. No one contested or opposed Sydenham's view of the Jesuits' powder. Cardinal de Lugo had been dead for eight years and there was no one to take up the defense of the drug, all mention of which, aside from Sydenham's rather casual remarks, had disappeared from medical literature both in England and on the Continent. The ague thus proceeded in its course undisturbed.

CHAPTER V

The Wonderful Secret of the Englishman

About the time that Thomas Sydenham published his *Method for Curing the Fevers* a most extraordinary rumor began to spread through England, originating on the coast of Essex, an extremely marshy region infested with the deadly ague. According to the rumor, there was a man in Essex who could cure the ague. Because the man was a quack the rumor at first was a negligible one. For centuries quackery had "specialized" in the ague, an unfailing source of income, and the ague curers were a regular feature of every town, village, and hamlet. Rumors of miraculous cures were always afloat: cures by charms, incantations, spells, prayers, astrology, amulets, stargazing, by every possible means that human ingenuity and dishonesty could devise. One anecdote narrated by Swift will give an idea of the kind of "specialist" who posed as an ague curer. Swift recounts the story: "I tell you a good pun: A fellow hard by pretends to cure agues, and has set out a sign, and spells it *egoes;* a gentleman and I observing it, he said, 'How does that fellow pretend to cure Agues?' I said, I did not know, but I was sure it was not by a *spell*."

As a rule, however, the rumors of those extraordinary cures were as ephemeral as the cures were ineffective. Yet in the case of the man from Essex the rumor persisted and it was of a rather peculiar nature. He was not a native of the place and claimed that he had settled in an ague-ridden region for the purpose of studying it and thus finding a way of curing it. This he did because, as he himself explained later on, "When I first started the study and practice of physick I met with a quartan ague, a disease that seemed to me the . . . folly and derision of my profession, did so exasperate my spirit that I was resolved to do what study or industry could perform to find out a certain method for the cure of this unruly distemper. . . . I consider it there was no other way to satisfy my desire but that good old way, observation and experiment." Strange behavior for a quack at a time when the words "observation and experiment" were unfortunately missing from the vocabulary of official medicine itself.

Furthermore the man was credited with a scholarly background and one of unquestionable respectability: his father had been registrar of the Bishop of Ely and his grandfather registrar of Cambridge University, where he himself had been admitted as a sizar in St. John's College, although his stay there seems to have been rather a short one. As far as his medical education was concerned, his requirements were somewhat flimsy, since his only connection with academic medicine was, unaccountably enough, that of having been an apprentice at the apothecary shop in Cambridge of a certain Mr. Dent. This probably explains the startling nature of his interpretation of medical phenomena.

A typical feature of the ague is the abnormal enlargement of the spleen, which can be felt from the outside and which was called in England the "ague cake." When the ague disappears the spleen goes back to its normal size. The Essex quack, however, pretended that the ague cake was the cause of the disease and that the patient got rid of it by expelling it from the body by way of the mouth. Thus his patients were phenomenal in that they could perform the unprecedented feat of spitting out their spleens.

These and other similar statements undoubtedly showed him up as a charlatan of the first water. Nevertheless, when it came to his method of treating the ague, his procedure was quite different from that of the typical ague curer. He dealt not with charms or incantations; he simply gave a medicine to be taken according to certain directions of a very unimpressive type, like a tablespoonful every three hours so many times a day, or something of the sort. He was opposed to bleeding, purged but little, and hardly ever gave emetics, which was another instance of his appalling lack of medical tradition, since he did not seem to be the least bit worried by the corrupt humors he so contentedly left within the body. Of Hippocrates and Galen he could have read but little, and so obviously he knew nothing of the theory of the balance of the humors.

Notwithstanding all these handicaps, his reputation continued to spread and he was frequently and clandestinely called to London in consultation. Thus encouraged, he decided to settle in the metropolis and about 1668 he started practice in London, styling himself a "pyretiatro," which literally meant a feverologist, or rather, a specialist in fevers. Very soon he became the city's fashionable quack and in order to maintain his prestige he published a book on fevers, even as all the great authorities on the subject before him had done. He had the title set in Greek characters to impress his readers with his learning and a laudatory poem was inserted which begins with the following pretty verses:

The Learned Author in a generous Fit,
T' oblige his Country hath of Agues Writ:

Physicians now shall be reproacht no more,
Nor Essex shake with Agues as before,
Since certain health salutes her sickly shoar.

The learned author then proceeds to deal with such diverse
and extraordinary things as a mysterious "sea-horse in Nilus,"
charms, which he classifies as "words of no sense which disturb
not the imagination; words of similitude that humored the
imagination; Scripture words that do strengthen the imagination," and Adam's knowledge of all plants, minerals, and animals, unfortunately lost in the "fall" by which, the faculties of
man's soul being depraved, "Memory is subject to fail, the
Judgment given to erre, and the Will often known to rebel,
and become a voluntary slave to passion." So man's body,
according to the author, became subject to many infirmities
and its preservation on earth as much a miracle as its creation,
though both surpass the scale of our reason, for reason, as
defined by the writer, "is at best but the harmony or musical
sound of a well tuned Hypothesis, wherewith the fancy is
delighted, and it suffers the same fate with our common
Musick; for as every tune delights not every ear, so every
reason pleases not every fancy."

Therefore, concludes the quack, nothing is certain in medicine and philosophy but mathematical and experimental dem-
onstrations, whereupon he proceeds to establish the difference
between the learned rational physician and the uneducated
modern empiric, the former having more law and reason than
experience to warrant his practice and the latter only "success," the result more of experience than reason, which practice he claims to be the surest, for "we find many strange
virtues in Plants, Stones, and Minerals, which our reason cannot
solve; and if we should therefore leave off the use of them, we

should do great injury to Mankind." Nevertheless, in order not to seem altogether "irrational and empiric," the ague curer gives his opinion as to the cause of agues and indeed all fevers, which, admittedly following the more famous of his contemporaries, he ascribes to the fermentation of the blood, caused by the action of some foreign matter, "like the fermentation of wine is caused by the addition into it of sugar or of any such substance." (If this curious parallel between the process of disease and the fermentation of wine was an original conception of the ague curer, there was some element of the prophet in him, for when two hundred years later this same parallel was made on an experimental basis it led to unique medical discoveries.)

In stating his views on the cause of the ague, however, the quack was only conforming with established customs, for, he wrote, "I know it will be expected by this curious Age, that I should be as happy in finding out the cause, as I have been successful in finding out the cure of this supposed unknown and uncurable disease. . . ." Yet when it came to explaining his method for achieving this cure his former clarity of exposition gives way to cabalistic forms of speech, concerning strange remedies made of nameless ingredients both indigenous and exotic, all of which ended by being utterly incomprehensible, the only clear statement being an irrelevant warning against the Peruvian bark: "Beware," he wrote, "of all palliative Cures, and especially of that known by the name of the Jesuits' Powder . . . for I have seen most dangerous effects follow the taking of that medicine." Thus in his published statements the quack from Essex showed that in this particular instance he was conforming with the accepted medical opinion of his time, although further on he seemed to contradict himself by adding: "Yet is this Powder not all together to be condemned; for it is a noble and safe medicine, if rightly prepared and corrected, and administered by a skilful hand. . . ."

Although the illegal practice of medicine was an established usage in the seventeenth century, the success attained in London by the Essex quack as an ague curer began to reach alarming proportions. In no time he had gained the favor of the great world and thus became an object of such great concern on the part of London's practitioners that the Royal College of Physicians began to show signs of agitated interest in his activities. Yet there was not much they could do; his method of treatment, for one thing, seemed to be harmless enough since no ill effects had been reported among his patients. As for the man himself, disregarding with olympian indifference the gathering storm, he continued with his illegal exercise of medicine, reaping wealth and climbing higher and higher on the social ladder. Such was the uncanny ability of this extraordinary man, whose name was Robert Talbor. Talbor's success showed how acute in England was the problem of malaria.

Time, however, went by and the medical world continued to ignore the Peruvian bark until the year 1676, when again Thomas Sydenham dwelt on the subject of the new drug in his *Medical Observations*. He seemed to have a better opinion of the bark this time, although he again expressed his fears for the life of the patient. Nevertheless he insisted on the fact that it was the sole remedy for the quartan fever, although he pointed out that the good effects were only temporary. As for the tertian, he recommended a regime based on purging and stimulating the patient to perspiration, without recourse to the new drug.

In spite of all his fears and apprehensions, Sydenham was now on the right path to discover the best way of administering the Jesuits' powder, recommending its *repeated* use during the periods of remission, contrary to his earlier, condescending suggestion that it might be given after the fever had subsided. His method was so far from perfect that it is no wonder he obtained such dubious results. Nevertheless, had he continued to develop it, he would have laid the foundation for the successful administration of quinine in all kinds of malarial fevers. But Sydenham's fortress of prejudices was built on too strong a foundation for unconditional surrender. Only by crossing a bridge here and storming a turret there could its strength be undermined.

The time was near at hand, however, when worse things would happen to the Jesuits' powder than Sydenham's reluctance to use it. England was a hotbed of religious dissensions. With a Catholic queen, a Catholic heir to the throne, and a very dubious Protestant king, the suspicions against the Roman Catholics had finally reached a stage of hysterical alarm. The situation was ideal for the customary activities of political factions which, for their own purposes, could make excellent use of the inevitable fanatics on both sides. Rumors of popish conspiracies and rebellions were constantly and diligently passed around with special emphasis on the Jesuits as the instigators and promoters of all impending disasters. Inexorably the popular mind was being aroused to a point where it would cry out for a real conspiracy in order to break up the unendurable suspense; when the right time came a conspiracy could easily be manufactured, and in the ensuing repression it would be easy to dispose of many an unwanted character. The time began to draw near about the spring of 1678, when the circulating rumors assumed an air of menacing reality. It seemed that there was indeed a conspiracy; names, dates, and definite purposes began to come into the open. The sordid nightmare that was to haunt Charles II for the rest of his life was taking its ugly shape in the corridors and antechambers of Whitehall.

However, in the midst of these ominous signs, when the tension had almost reached its breaking point, a figure thoroughly unaffected and to all appearances quite unconcerned with the prevailing religious or political dissensions suddenly slipped into the limelight. In the spring of 1678 London's famous and fashionable quack Robert Talbor, formerly from Essex, proved to be an object of very special attention on the part of a worried monarch. This is attested by a letter addressed to the Royal College of Physicians by Lord Arlington, Secretary of State, on behalf of His Majesty Charles II, King of England: "His Majesty, having received great satisfaction in the abilities . . . of Dr. Talbor for the cure of agues has caused him to be admitted and sworn one of his physicians; and, being graciously inclined to give him all favour and assistance . . . for the public good, has commanded me to signify his pleasure unto you and the rest of the college of physicians that you should not give him any molestation or disturbance in his practice. . . ."

Loud and sorrowful indeed must have been the lamentations of the English medical profession at this unheard-of affront and humiliation. But they were quite wasted. The king, if he heard them, as he probably did, must have enjoyed them tremendously. Charles II was a cynic who had learned through long years of exile and poverty the appreciation of intrinsic values. The quack had cured him of a "malignant fever" against which his learned physicians had been powerless for years. Admitting in all probability that his physicians knew best, the king simply wanted to be treated by the man who did better. There was nothing that the Royal College of Physicians could do but cover itself with ashes and tear its garments at the disgrace that befell it in the elevation to honor and splendor of the despicable ague curer.

That was only the beginning of Talbor's amazing success. Having insured his professional status, the king proceeded to the establishment of his social position. With the customary ceremonial the ague curer was knighted in Whitehall by His Majesty and thus became Sir Robert Talbor, physician to the king. What a unique and wonderful man this Talbor must have been! Physician to the king and author of books about Adam's scientific achievements and the mythical "sea-horse in Nilus"! Yet in the eyes of the medical world of his day all of Sir Robert's nonsense was negligible compared to the unspeakable heresy of his method for treating the ague; because Sir Robert Talbor had not improved in his reverence for the classics as he improved in the graces of the world. He still did not bleed his patients, purged but little, and hardly ever gave emetics. The great theory of the balance of the humors, the ill effects of the bile, the very basis of medicine, the explanation of all causes of disease were disregarded by this incredible ignoramus. Hippocrates and Galen and the great Avicenna must have turned in their graves at the success of the impostor. Yet he was not so much to blame. At the time these great authors could be read only in Latin texts and Sir Robert Talbor in all probability was not too fluent in the dead tongues of antiquity. Disgruntled as the London physicians must have been at the king's unprecedented action, the very peculiar case of Sir Robert Talbor would no doubt eventually have stirred some sort of activity in the ranks of this learned profession. But then came the "Popish Plot," and Sir Robert Talbor left the English nation to travel in foreign lands.

The most accurately timed murder ever committed in history was that of Sir Edmund Berry Godfrey, a magistrate of the peace, to whom had been entrusted the deposition, duly sworn by the greatest madman that ever lived, containing all the information of the long-advertised Popish Plot. Obviously no one but the papists could have done away with the righteous magistrate, because he knew how they were going to murder the king in order to put his Catholic brother on the throne, and how they were going to raise an army in order to flood the English nation with Protestant blood. The papists did it; that is, the Jesuits did it. They murdered Sir Edmund Berry Godfrey, who was going to expose their black deeds to the sober judgment of the English people; and the English people indulged in a none too sober display. The general outcry was indescribable. The Jesuits then were the hidden terror which had kept them for so long in the power of fear. The Jesuits wanted to assassinate the king! The Jesuits were planning the slaughter of all the Protestants in England! The Jesuits wanted to poison the whole world! . . . The Jesuits were already poisoning the whole world by means of an outlandish, so-called medicine, commonly known as the Jesuits' powder. And so the Peruvian bark, or the facsimile of it, was paraded through the streets of London with great signs telling the gruesome story of how the Jesuits were using it to exterminate the non-Jesuit population.

Little knew my Lord Shaftesbury, the leader of His Majesty's Opposition, that in goading the English people with non-existent plots to the extremes of untold cruelty he nearly deprived them for many years of a remedy which was to be one of the main factors in a great enterprise the English people had recently undertaken. In 1601 the English had started the first trading posts in India, but this commercial venture did not expand very far because the Portuguese, who already had great concessions firmly established there, knew the terrain too well for any outsider to step easily into it. It was not until after 1663 that the English gained a strong foothold in India when the Portuguese princess whom Charles II had married—the Catholic Queen of England whom Lord Shaftesbury hated so much—had brought as dowry the right for the English people to trade in the Portuguese concessions. And malaria was too widespread in India for anyone to trade successfully without large amounts of quinine at hand, as the British soldiers and the agents of the East India Company were to discover to their great distress.

My Lord Shaftesbury nearly did away with His Gracious Majesty, and Charles II certainly swallowed a bitter cup in the autumn of 1678. Yet when everything looked gloomiest the king again took the time to occupy himself very particularly with the welfare of Sir Robert Talbor. Sir Robert's success in treating the king apparently had been so overwhelming that Charles II, in spite of his predicament, felt compelled to share the unexpected blessing. Having lived for many years in the French court, he knew how everybody there suffered from the ague and how the royal family was being decimated by a great variety of feverish diseases. At the moment the dauphin, the only remaining son of Louis XIV, was seriously ill with a pernicious fever. Charles, who had always been on very close terms with the King of France, decided to send his personal physician to Paris to see what he could do for the fever-stricken prince, so with all the honors due to a royal envoy Sir Robert set out for the court of France.

But now that Sir Robert had become the physician of kings and princesses in profusion, a question came into the open: what was his method of treatment? What was he giving or intending to give his royal charges? Whenever a king was going to be subjected to a special treatment it was customary for the physician in charge to hold a consultation with the other royal physicians and ask their agreement to the procedure he intended to follow. Moreover the physicians would notify the council of the Crown of whatever drugs or other measures they were to use. The council, on the other hand, could forbid any risky procedures that might seem unnecessary, thus guaranteeing the immunity of the physician and the safety of the king. All these precautionary measures had been devised to offer a solution to a situation that had become practically insoluble. In early times physicians were slain for their failure in curing kings, and as late as the seventeenth century they could be severely punished should they make any decision by themselves even in a case of the greatest emergency. Thus many a king had died in utter misery and even unnecessarily because, as soon as he began to look really sick, no one had dared to give him so much as a glass of water.

Usages and protocols had evidently been disregarded in the case of Sir Robert Talbor. He did not require in his practice the consent of his colleagues and he did not tell any council what he intended to do, for the very simple reason that the method he so successfully used for the cure of the ague was a "secret." After years of observation and experiment in a malarial region he had found out this secret of which he was the sole discoverer. It had been a laborious and even dangerous enterprise. He was willing to treat anyone who could pay for it but he refused to let others profit by it. The kings of Europe would have to make their choice: either to suffer from the "fevers" or to trust themselves implicitly in his hands. Sir Robert Talbor was quite willing to assume the entire responsibility for whatever the results might be.

The results were amazing. Talbor's success in France was unique. In no time the dauphin was cured of his fever. In no time, if the statements of contemporaries are to be credited, the whole royal family was cured by the ministrations of Sir Robert Talbor. The court was spellbound. He was addressed as "Chevalier" and, adapting himself to the new surroundings, he changed his name from Talbor to Talbot, having learned that the latter was a French name of distinguished origin. And the Chevalier Talbot managed so well in that highly cultivated milieu that both he and his secret became the great vogue of the day.

The Queen of Spain became ill with the "fevers"; immediately the chevalier was sent by Louis XIV to the Spanish court. The Queen of Spain was cured without difficulty and Sir Robert Talbot returned in splendor to France. The court talked of nothing else; how "Monseigneur" and "Mme. la Dauphine" had been cured was the endless topic of conversation. The court was jubilant. Not only was the royal family delivered of its fevers, but the chevalier's magic cures had also created a situation which could not help but delight the courtiers of Louis XIV. Among these shone some of the most devastating wits of that age when the salutary art of ridiculing human folly in all its forms reached heights never attained before or since. And no better instance of human folly could be offered to the court than the spectacle of Louis XIV's physicians witnessing in amazement the medical feats performed by the chevalier. It was inevitable therefore that they should have become a perfect source of inspiration for the court's wits, whose epigrams and songs ridiculing them and praising Talbot were eagerly passed around and, according to Mme. de Sévigné, repeated by the merry Count of Gramont in the very face of pathetic Daquin, the king's private physician, who in all probability wished he were dead.

Needless to say, the court physicians were very much annoyed with the chevalier. The whole thing was incredible; he entered the sick man's room, produced his secret, a winy-tasting liquid, as a magician pulls rabbits out of his hat, gave it to the patient, and that was that; a sedative, perhaps, to bring about restful sleep. A few more doses of the secret and the fever was definitely gone. It was preposterous. It was against all established rules; the man was an impostor. Their mournful protests, however, were quite wasted; popular opinion at court sided with the chevalier.

Mme. de Sévigné herself, who had always held official medicine in contempt, became the chevalier's fervent devotee. In her letters she went into raptures about *le remède de l'Anglais* and *l'Anglais* himself, of whom she said that he was *un homme divin*, deserving a temple like Aesculapius. Her joy at the court physicians' predicament had no limits. "The remedy of the Englishman makes them quite contemptible with all their bloodletting," she wrote. "It is to take life itself away from them to take fevers from their domain." Later on she added: "Only the three or four physicians who recommend the remedy of the Englishman are held in esteem at the court"; she was delighted.

She made terrible scenes at the deathbeds of her friends, fighting with the doctors in charge to have the Englishman called. It can be rightly assumed that she made quite a nuisance of herself, as in the case of Cardinal de Retz, who, being very ill, was bled to death by his physician. "Mme. de Lafayette, my daughter, and I cry to them to have pity; . . . but no one would undertake the responsibility of bringing the Englishman," she wrote, telling the story. Finally the chevalier was brought in and, looking down on the dying cardinal, stated in a grand manner that he could not resuscitate the dead. Even he had his limitations.

Mme. de Sévigné was relentless; yet she had a sore failure with her friend M. d'Hautefort, who was so stingy that he is considered to be the original of Molière's *L'Avare*. Being at death's door, he had refused to take the remedy of the Englishman because it was too expensive, although everyone around him begged him to do it, assuring him that it would save his life. "Monsieur, it is only forty *pistoles*," he was told at the last minute. "It is too much," he answered with a supreme effort, and died. A M. d'Hautefort, however, was a mere trifle to the chevalier, who, in addition to royalty, was treating such great men as La Rochefoucauld, author of the *Maximes,* and Colbert, the all-powerful Minister of Finance of Louis XIV.

Sir Robert Talbot's success in the French court was probably unique in the history of quackery; yet to insure that success the stage had been set beforehand by one of the greatest playwrights of all times. Only five years before Talbot went to France, Molière's *Le Malade imaginaire* had been put on the stage. It was a tremendous success. In this play Molière made a most devastating attack on the medicine of his time. He ridiculed not only the mannerisms of the physicians—their wigs, their frocks, and their speech—but also the doctrines on which their medicine was based, the old medical doctrines of the Galenic school. Galenism at the time, thanks to the works of Vesalius and Harvey, was a walking skeleton. Molière buried it and the funeral was a great occasion; from then on it was a ghost. By putting on the stage the Galenic physician with his mummified ideas, Molière made the people aware of the anachronism he represented.

And the people laughed. They laughed at the usage of Latin in order to impress the patient, at the constant purging and bleeding for every disease, and at the hero's desire to get rid of his bile, which Hippocrates had considered to be the cause of all fevers. They laughed at the measures used to deliver the sick man of his corrupt humors; and so they laughed at the theory of the balance of the humors. They laughed at the young physician who wrote the thesis against Harvey's discovery of the circulation of the blood; and so they laughed at the Faculty of Medicine of Paris, which was violently "anti-circulationist." And last of all they laughed at the final scene, in which a mocking ceremony of conferring the doctor's degree takes place.

"Dost thou swear to follow the advice of the ancients whether good or bad? Dost thou swear not to use any other remedy but those used by the Faculty even if the patient should die?" the doctors to be were asked. The mirth of the audience was indescribable. The people laughed; the king laughed, and thereupon the court roared with laughter. And they were still laughing when the Chevalier Talbot appeared with his secret; then they went into hysterics.

With his peculiar medical ideas, the chevalier was the living negation of that medicine which Molière, with the insight of genius, had mercilessly torn to bits on the stage. "If only Molière were alive," wrote Mme. de Sévigné, commenting on the discomfiture of the king's physicians at Talbot's performance. If Molière had been alive, for once he would have laughed in the audience. Because the progress of the chevalier with his secret through the courts of Europe was as good a farce as he himself could have invented; and, as a professional, he would have bowed to Talbot's perfect *mise en scène* and superb acting.

Finally the chevalier's farce was at an end; only the last grand scene remained to be enacted. Louis XIV decided to buy Sir Robert Talbot's secret. Sir Robert agreed on condition that the secret would not be made public until after his death. The king accepted these terms. He paid Talbot three thousand gold crowns and a substantial pension for life for the right to publish the secret for the welfare of his subjects.

Thereupon this physician of kings, a rich and powerful man, returned to England to become the recipient of many honors and distinctions, among them that of being made a fellow commoner of St. John's College at Cambridge University. A few months later, in the year 1681, Sir Robert Talbot died. He was only forty-two years of age, and unfortunately the world could never know what extraordinary things he might have accomplished had his magnificent career not been cut short.

In January 1682 the King of France had a book published revealing the secret; this was immediately translated into English with the title, *The English Remedy: or, Talbor's Wonderful Secret, for Cureing of Agues and Feavers*. The secret was the Jesuits' powder, referred to in the book as quinquina, mixed with wine—always a different kind of wine in order to disguise its identity. How much of a stir this revelation caused is not known, but it was certain to have been considerable. Speculation about his cure had sprung up again after Talbor's return from France, and there is evidence that the philosopher-mathematician, Leibnitz, had communicated to Nehemiah Grew, the eminent English botanist, a bit of interesting gossip to the effect that "Talbor's Secret was the Jesuits' Powder," and Grew in turn saw fit to pass this bit of conjecture on to his fellow scientists at a formal meeting of the Royal Society. Whether they approved of him or not, the great figures of his time certainly talked about Sir Robert Talbor.

The task begun in good faith by Cardinal de Lugo was now accomplished twenty-two years after his death by means which the cardinal would have considered most objectionable but which a philosopher would have appreciated in its full value. Quinine was now introduced into medicine by the man who had found by cunning and artfulness the way of defeating prejudice and intolerance, but who had also found by observation and experiment the proper way of administering the drug. The event was properly celebrated in France by a poetical venture called *Le Poème du quinquina,* written by the fabulist, La Fontaine. In evaluating the importance of this innovation in medicine, La Fontaine gave proof once again of the versatility of his genius. The subject, however, had obviously failed to stir him and the resultant medical verses were by no means inspired even though they had been undertaken at the behest of the beautiful Duchess of Bouillon, herself a former victim of the ague.

One point concerning Talbor's life has so far remained wrapped in complete mystery. By what devious ways did he obtain the bark for his experiments in Essex, ways that no one was able to fathom? Was his former employer, Mr. Dent, supplying him secretly with the drug? Throughout all his life the secret acquisition of the bark must have been a considerable problem to Sir Robert but he apparently managed it with unusual ability and a fair amount of ruthlessness.

In the French book revealing the secret the author, a dubious medical character named Nicholas de Blegny, states that when the English remedy became famous in France Sir Robert, in order to stop anyone from experimenting with the bark and thus by chance discovering his secret, had bought all that was available in France and England. Hence he made the first attempt to "corner the market," and the price of quinine rose from twenty-five to one hundred francs a pound. This attempt to place the bark beyond the reach of all save himself was far from laudable. Yet it was the inevitable consequence of his also far from laudable procedure of keeping the remedy secret, although, judging from the academic standards of his time, it did not place him beyond the pale when so punctilious a university as Cambridge saw fit to honor him on his return from France.

To be sure, it is questionable whether the secrecy was a premeditated move, and there are good reasons to believe that in the course of time he found himself in desperate need of hiding the identity of the remedy. He, who was not a physician, was working with a drug labeled by the medical profession as dangerous, one which exposed those who used it to the perilous accusation of popery, and which was finally decried by the mobs as the Jesuits' poison. It is only logical to conclude that many a physician in England had shrunk from using the drug out of sheer panic of its unpleasant connotations. Considering these circumstances, it may be that Talbor performed an act of unusual courage. He was giving the

Jesuits' powder to Charles II at the precise moment when the Jesuits were publicly accused of wanting to murder the king and when the court physicians, of which he was one, were under suspicion since the queen's own physician, Dr. Wakeman, was a prisoner accused of planning to poison the king. Dr. Wakeman, a papist, was obviously an ideal person on whom to pin the murderous attempt, since the ugly accusation was aimed at the queen herself. Yet even the forged evidence against him was flimsy, whereas to convict Talbor would have been child's play. If, by one of these accidents of destiny, the king had happened to die at that moment and attention had been focused on Sir Robert, as it undoubtedly would have been, he would have paid for his temerity with a terrible death.

The king, who had never believed in Jesuits' plots, let alone Jesuits' poisons, must have known the remedy employed by Talbor. Thus he was fully aware of the danger surrounding Sir Robert, for he knew that the inventors of the plot were in desperate need of a plausible scapegoat. And Charles II, who has been decried as an ungrateful monarch, must have had the welfare of his physician in mind when he deprived himself of Talbor's services, precious as they were to him, knowing only too well that if Lord Shaftesbury should lay hands on him, only God could help him. And so he sent Sir Robert to the court of France. As a result Lord Shaftesbury, who was producing the most unconvincing murderers, missed the unique chance given to him by the temerity of the ague curer. While Sir Robert was in Paris Charles II was taken very ill with an attack of malaria, but he made no attempt to recall to his bedside the physician in whom he had the greatest confidence. This illness of Charles II in fact seems to have shaken the English people to the realization that with all his faults he was better than those who, by emphasizing religious differences, had had no hesitation in driving the English nation to the brink of a civil war in order to succeed with their political intrigues. On the king's recovery the English people rejoiced; plots and conspiracies were gradually forgotten; popular frenzy against the Jesuits began to subside and Sir Robert Talbor, the danger passed, returned with his secret to the English nation.

In spite of all the precautions taken by Sir Robert to protect his secret, others as well as the highly placed Leibnitz had obviously guessed what it was all about. While Talbor was in Paris a book appeared in that city called *Of the Cure of Fevers by the Quinquina,* written by François de Monginot, a Parisian practitioner and a man of high learning. In this book an exceedingly pointed reference appears concerning some who made a secret of the Peruvian bark and used it with little sense and much daring; the book sold like wildfire, four editions of it being printed in one year—thus turning it into a "best seller" of its time. Yet Monginot's book was hardly necessary because Talbor's own statement in 1672, that "the Jesuits' powder was a noble and safe medicine when rightly prepared and administered by skilful hands," ought to have been fairly illuminating.

So illuminating was it in fact that the light it shed may be the key to a rather peculiar incident. In the year 1677, a few months before Talbor was knighted, Thomas Sydenham wrote the following paragraph in one of his letters:

I have had but few trials, but I am sure that an ounce of bark, given between the two fits, cures; which the physicians in London not being pleased to take notice of in my book, or not believing

me, have given an opportunity to a fellow that was but an apothecary's man, to go away with all the practice on Agues, by which
he has gotten an estate in two months, and brought great reproach
on the faculty.

These petty remarks, which could apply only to Talbor,
seemed to show that Sydenham knew the real nature of Talbor's secret although he never exposed him by name.

Rumor would have it that if Sydenham knew the secret it
was because Talbor himself had told him and that he had also
told him of his method for administering the bark; hence
Sydenham's improvement in his administration of the drug.
Whether this was true or not is a matter for conjecture, but
even if it was not, Sydenham's bitterness at the opportunities
given to the "apothecary's man" was most unjustified. At the
time when he had casually dismissed the drug as a dangerous
remedy Talbor was already famous in Essex for his success
in curing the ague, as Sydenham well knew, although so unconcerned was he with the new remedy that he failed completely to connect it with the extraordinary method of the
ague curer, whom he righteously denounced in the following
passage appearing in his *Method for Curing the Fevers:* "If
any one conceals a method, or a specific medicine, by which
autumnal intermittents are curable, he deserves neither the
name of a good citizen, nor of a prudent man." This was in
1666; in 1668 the second edition of Sydenham's book appeared with no changes concerning the author's bad opinion
of the drug. In 1672, Talbor, now famous in London, published his book stating that the Jesuits' powder was a noble
medicine . . . if administered by a *skillful* hand, and four
years later Sydenham's *Medical Observations* appeared, showing that he had had "a few trials" with the bark. In 1680 he

made a definite claim to having discovered the proper method for its administration, affirming in addition that he had always regarded the drug as both a harmless and most effective remedy. This last statement seems to indicate in Sydenham a certain fickleness of memory; evidently infuriated at his own hesitations over the efficacy of the bark, now so definitely proven by a "quack," he mistook what he had not done for what he wished he had done—a well-known error indeed, but occurring usually in people of far less stature than Sydenham.

After Talbor's secret was published, however, it became quite obvious that Sydenham's claim would be accepted only by those who deliberately wanted to accept it. The eminent naturalist, John Ray, for example, although greatly admiring Sydenham, definitely stated in his *History of Plants* that the world was indebted to Robert Talbor for having revived the use of the Peruvian bark after it had fallen into disuse. To be sure, Ray was not a physician and his acknowledgment of Talbor's achievement did not reflect on his professional dignity. Thus the only contemporary testimony of authority in favor of Talbor is to be found in a book of natural history and not in a book of medicine where it belonged.

Talbor's definite demonstration of the effectiveness of the Peruvian bark was the first and basic step in the solution of the world-wide problem of malaria. The medical profession, however, made heroic efforts to ignore it at the time. In France three generations of Louis XIV's children were to die before official medicine decided to adopt the use of the so-called English remedy. In England, one year after Talbor's death, Charles II had another bad attack of malaria. His physicians proceeded to the customary bleeding and purging while the king begged them to give him Talbor's remedy. In despair he sent a secret message to a Dr. Short, asking him for his opinion. Dr. Short's answer was that only quinine could save his life. Thereupon Charles commanded his physicians to give him the remedy and they were forced to comply. Lord Normanby told Evelyn, who wrote the story in his diary, that he asked the physicians why they refused the drug. According to Evelyn's own words, "Dr. Lower said that it would spoil their practice, or some such expression."

The illnesses of Charles II are well known to have been the occasion for all sorts of intrigues, cabals, and petty rivalries. His Anglican ministers claimed the monopoly of his soul and thus kept a constant watch for fear that he might request the last rites of the Roman Church; his physicians claimed the monopoly of his body, which they tortured beyond belief, and while forbidding him the Jesuits' powder they gave him drops of extract of human skull, physics, and emetics at a murderous rate, bled him white through the shoulder, raised blisters on his scalp, and put plasters of pitch and pigeon dung on his feet. It is a great comfort to know that he fooled both his ministers and his physicians. That Charles II had a poor opinion of his fellow men is no wonder. If in protecting Talbor he deliberately insulted the medical profession it would be less wonder.

The English physicians bitterly resented Talbor, and when confronted with the inevitable acceptance of the ague curer's contribution they clung desperately to the unexpected blessing of Sydenham's claim. Even those contemporaries who disliked Sydenham most hailed him as the discoverer of the method for administering the Peruvian bark. As such he has come down to posterity and as such he has been praised as the introducer of this priceless remedy.

As for Talbor, after his death they called him "a debauched apothecary's apprentice," "seller of secrets," and "ignorant empiric." Empiric he was indeed but ignorant he was not. His contribution to medicine was not limited to the revival of quinine, for he gave the first practical demonstration that Galenic medicine was basically wrong. By refusing to bleed and purge his patients he discarded the idea that it was necessary to deliver the sick man from theoretical corrupt humors, since it was obvious to him that the drug itself could cure, and with far better results. How this happened he did not try to explain for the very good reason that he did not know. Thus he behaved like a modern man of science: like the men who in our days have introduced into medicine the sulpha drugs and penicillin, the quinines of the twentieth century. They know that these drugs cure but they do not know how they cure; time and research have been lavishly spent in trying to elucidate the way in which quinine cures malaria, and a definite answer is still to come. Meanwhile, following Talbor's original method, untold numbers of lives have been saved by its empirical administration.

With Sir Robert Talbor and the final introduction of quinine begins the era of the practical application of rational empiricism in medicine, the foundations of which had been laid by Francis Bacon. This was the great contribution of England to the progress of the medical sciences. The Galenic physician of Molière, who astounded his patients with his brilliant tirades as to the causes of their diseases, had to bow himself out and leave the stage to a quiet man who carried a box of pills in a celebrated black leather bag. And the first successful pill doctor on record is Sir Robert Talbor, who carried his secret about, surely not in a black leather bag, but presumably in some ornate arrangement of baroque design embroidered in petit point by Mme. de Sévigné.

Sir Robert Talbor, a great empiric, was repudiated by his contemporaries, scorned and quickly forgotten by posterity. In the medical world he became the traditional skeleton in the closet; very seldom has he been mentioned in the literature and always incidentally, usually being dismissed as an amazingly clever quack who did well in the great world. Once or twice mention of praise has been found, but interestingly enough it has always come from persons of great distinction who, in all fairness, insisted on giving the devil his due.

Sir Robert no doubt foresaw this and to remedy the situation he proceeded to establish some imperishable testimony of his great worth, for the enlightenment of future generations. Thus shortly before he died he erected for his family a monument in Trinity Church, Cambridge, in which he rightly describes himself as the "most honorable Robert Talbor, Knight and Singular Physician, unique in curing Fevers of which he had delivered Charles II King of England, Louis XIV King of France, the Most Serene Dauphin, Princes, many a Duke and a large number of lesser personages."

CHAPTER VI

The Fever Bark Tree

In the year 1785 an illustrious English physician named Sir George Baker read to the College of Physicians a paper dealing with the ague to which was added a short history of the Peruvian bark. Sir George, who has been described as a man "possessed of a peculiar judgment and penetration, united with a liberality, and candour, which could not fail to engage the friendship and esteem of his contemporaries," ended his paper with the following paragraph:

Had it not been for the casual experience of an uncivilized people, it might never have been discovered, that there existed, in the stores of nature, a specific febrifuge. Had not the influence of a great religious society, unconnected with the practice of physic, counteracted prevailing prejudices, at an early period, this medicine, though brought into Europe, might have long remained in obscurity, unknown, and useless. And lastly, had not physicians been taught by a man, whom they, both abroad and at home, vilified, as an ignorant empiric, we might, at this day, have had a powerful instrument in our hands, without knowing how to use it in the most effectual manner.

Sir George Baker is the only English physician known to have rejected Sydenham's claims and to have given Talbor the credit he deserved, thus offering undeniable proof of the liberality of his mind and of his "peculiar judgment." His remarks on the sad role played by the medical profession in connection with the introduction of the new remedy are certainly justified. But how severely is man to be condemned for his failure to see beyond the limited horizon of the beliefs of his time? For centuries physicians bled people to death, but for centuries also they bled themselves to death; a famous professor of medicine in Paris is said to have bled himself seventy times in the course of an attack of rheumatism. The physicians of the seventeenth century opposed the new drug according to their knowledge and beliefs, firmly convinced that it was a harmful substance. They may thus be exonerated of the charges of prejudice and intolerance in view of the sincerity attending their position.

To see beyond the beliefs of his time man has to do far more than strain his eyes in order to focus his sight on a distant point. The enveloping mists of established principles are too dense to be pierced by the human eye, and man has to journey through them to see what is beyond; in this attempt he braves in the dark the oceans of prejudice and intolerance which they hide and where so many, caught unaware, have been engulfed forever. The wonder, in fact, is that any man ever dares to cross the dangerous zone, and usually it is some extraordinary circumstance that impels him to face the rigors of an uncharted voyage.

It took two men who were not physicians to introduce quinine into medicine. Their judgment had not been dulled by the accumulated superstitions of the past, and so their vision was clear enough at least to guess what the truth might be. Both were men with unlimited ambitions, one for spiritual rewards, the other for material gain; Cardinal de Lugo failed in mid-journey, Sir Robert Talbor went triumphantly across, and those who remained behind, after gazing unmoved at the wreckage of the former, frowned in righteous disapproval at the means employed by the latter to evade the threatening waves. It is not often that resistance to material progress has been overcome by a ruse; however unwitting that resistance might be, bloodshed and misery have swept the earth on its account more than once and then has come a horrifying awakening. Yet the story repeats itself with tragic regularity because, as someone has said, "Man is the only animal who stumbles again on the same stone." Nevertheless, if it is within the laws of nature that man should be deprived of the ability to recognize the old stone, he should not be blamed too severely for falling flat on his nose at every twist on the road to progress. Instead of wondering at the absurdities of the physicians of the seventeenth century in opposing the new remedy, one should rather wonder at the acumen, foresight, and courage of Cardinal de Lugo and Sir Robert Talbor, to whom we owe the introduction into medicine of one of the most needed of all remedies.

In 1692, ten years after Talbor's death, the first books dealing rationally with the new remedy began to appear in England, one by Richard Morton and another by Martin Lister, both converts to the use of the drug after having opposed it. Neither Morton nor Lister, however, gave any credit to Talbor for having devised the proper method of using the bark; both treated him as a despicable charlatan, and Lister, in more forceful terms, also attacked Sydenham by saying that if the latter had never succeeded in handling the new remedy it was because he had *borrowed* the ague curer's procedure. Morton made the worst accusation ever brought against the medical profession by stating that the opposition to the bark was mainly the result of a conspiracy between physicians and apothecaries who resented the cure of a disease which had been for so long an unmixed financial blessing.

Four years later, in 1696, the bark was formally introduced into Germany by Conrad Peyer and Michele Bernard Valentini. And in the year 1711 there appeared the first complete treatise on its medicinal properties, written by an Italian physician named Francesco Torti, who made a contribution of the greatest importance as a result of his study of the bark and introduced the term "malaria" into medical literature. By observing the varying effect of the drug in the treatment of malarial fevers he was able to differentiate their diverse clinical forms and thus was the first to describe pernicious malaria, together with its proper form of treatment. Torti established with absolute certainty the fact that the bark was useless for all types of fever other than malaria. On this basis he refuted the universally accepted principle that all fevers were caused by the same agency; if this were so, the bark should be effective in all of them. With his work he gave final confirmation to the statement of his countryman and contemporary, Ramazzini, that the introduction of the bark was to be to medicine what gunpowder had been to the art of war. The literature written on the Peruvian bark from the time of Torti to the present day would fill a good-sized library.

At a period, however, when the scientific world undertook a thorough study of the new drug, which became an object of the greatest interest to the physician, the chemist, the botanist, and the naturalist alike, a peculiar feature of the bark baffled all efforts to arrive at a better understanding of its properties. This was the extreme and unpredictable variation in the effectiveness of different pieces of bark even though they all seemed to look exactly alike. The first explanation given to this phenomenon was the obvious one: that the merchants threw in all kinds of spurious barks. Cardinal de Lugo himself had already voiced the fear that when the bark was used in Rome in large quantities the urge for profit might induce the merchants, who bought it from the Jesuits, to countenance its adulteration. But an English physician named Gideon Harvey, disagreeing with this, reached some very provocative conclusions.

Dr. Harvey, who was the last sworn enemy of the bark, wrote a book in 1685 which is probably one of the most extraordinary literary performances in the whole history of medicine and which bears the following suggestive title: *The Conclave of Physicians, Detecting their intrigues, frauds, and plots, against their patients. Also a peculiar discourse of the Jesuits' Bark.* Dr. Harvey began his "peculiar discourse of the Bark" by saying that in dwelling on the subject he was only trying to help the patients and not "an ungrateful and most perverse sort of man (such as the profession generally fosters)."

In describing the effects of the Jesuits' powder, the use of which, according to Dr. Harvey, had been most unfortunately revived by "a debauched apothecary's apprentice of Cambridge," he stated:

On great numbers it Engenders Hypocondriack vapours, Scurvy, Obstructions, and tumours of the Spleen and Liver, ill habits of Body, Dropsies, Swelly Legs, Head-aches, suppression of Menstrua in Women, difficulties of breathing, Phtysicks, Palsies, and other great Distempers of the Brain, which possible are never afterwards to be removed: . . . Notwithstanding some Physick Ducklings are so fond of this monstrous Powder, that they prescribe it Panacea. . . .

Dr. Harvey thereupon indulged in some sorrowful lamentations upon the death of a nameless French "Monseigneur," who was apparently "of most illustrious extraction, whose life expressed a true Portrait of the Valour of the *Macedonian*, and Prudence of *Augustus* in *Martial* Affairs, no less at Sea than at Land" but who, having been given the Jesuits' powder with a liberal hand, was "Jesuited out of his Being." This criminal aberration on the part of the physicians Dr. Harvey could explain only on the grounds that "they imagine the Jesuits by Imprecations, Exorcisms, and Charms on their *Bark*, have made use of their Cloven-footed Master." But, he added, "to take off that aspersion from these poor Holy Fathers, I am of opinion, it is stupidity and ignorance in School learning, Philosophy, and the true Art of Physick, that impels these pretended Doctors to take their refuge to such occult causes, which to men of more serene capacity may be rendered sufficiently manifest."

Dr. Harvey then, making use of his "serene capacity," discussed the very pertinent question as to what the real nature of the Jesuits' powder actually was since, aside from the fact that it came from Peru, in the Spanish colonies, and that the parcels bore the name of the Jesuit fathers, no one knew "what tree or shrub it's excuriated from, what Fruit or Flower it bears. . . . Whether it is only growing in the kingdom of Peru," and, most important of all, whether the Bark was "artificial or natural," his opinion being that "none of it (though the best) arrives to us in its *puris naturalibus*, the tree spoken of, or some other like it, affording nothing but the Wood, into which the bitter Taste is immitted, by macerating it a convenient time in the Juyce of a certain *Indian* Plant, to which that penetrating bitterness is peculiar." Thus

Dr. Harvey reached the startling conclusion that the Jesuits' powder was an artificially faked product undoubtedly contrived by the industry of the Jesuit fathers. Considering the number of ailments, distempers, tumors, and disturbances caused by the bark, according to Dr. Harvey, his accusation was a great tribute to the manifold ability of the Jesuits to manipulate chemically the manufacture of the bark.

It is doubtful whether any serious consideration was given to this statement of Dr. Harvey's. Yet the fact remained, as he had rightly said, that no one knew anything about the plant from which the bark came. Nothing could better illustrate the confusion surrounding the natural origins of the drug than the fact that the new remedy did not even have a designation of its own. Like a foundling, it had been given the name of its sponsor of the moment—from the Countess's powder to Talbor's Wonderful Secret. It had also been called several names like Indian powder and Peruvian bark to designate its place of origin, and different variations of quinquina and quina-quina to give it what might sound like an aboriginal name. The latter was really the name of another medicinal plant, also from Peru, and thus some authors had discussed the curative virtues of the authentic quina-quina, believing it to be the new anti-malarial. The list of synonyms was endless and the ways of spelling them infinite, including China-China, used by some authors in the belief that the drug came from China.

In order to give the new remedy a legitimate status, a botanical classification of the plant from which it came was imperative. Meanwhile some believed it to be a shrub, though the majority were in favor of a tree variously described as similar to the apple tree, the cherry tree, or the almond tree, for even after a hundred years of using the Peruvian bark, no one had ever seen the mysterious tree. The question, therefore, of whether there actually was such a tree was a legitimate one; but the answer was not easy to find. If such a tree existed, it was hidden in the immensity of the South American forests, the dangers of which filled the hearts of brave men with fear. No one, whether foreign or native, had ever dared to enter those forests but the wild aborigines who inhabited them. The missionaries, however, had come in contact with these forest Indians, and thus the only possible explanation of this curious situation seemed to be that the Indians were supplying the Jesuit missionaries with the bark; and, being a primitive lot, they were probably unable to give information about the trees to the fathers, the only white men ever to have commerce with them. Or perhaps they were reluctant to let it be known where the coveted trees could be found so that this forest refuge might be kept safe for them. And no sane man would want to oppose the wishes of the children of the wilderness unless fully equipped to cope with a variety of unpredictable emergencies. In such circumstances the search for the tree, assuming there was one, required a regular expedition and the offices of an expert botanist who would also be a courageous man, imbued with the spirit of adventure, and not afraid of snake, tick, bug, mosquito, spider, scorpion, swamp, fever, wild Indian or endless journeys.

Strangely enough, neither the Spanish Government nor the Jesuits, who were most directly concerned with the problem of the drug, seemed too eager about the problem of the tree. As far as the Jesuits were concerned, they were probably beginning to wash their hands of the whole affair, because by the middle of the eighteenth century the export of the drug had become the concern solely of the Spanish Government. And the Spanish Government, as governments have done before and since, failed to see the basis on which rested the future of one of its main enterprises as well as a matter of the greatest importance to the welfare of mankind.

So the years went by with physicians continuing to complain of the quality of the bark, one shipment being thoroughly effective, another absolutely useless. The problem of the dosage was an almost insoluble one, and the question was once again revived as to whether the bark had any medical virtue at all. The world still knew nothing of the fever bark tree, which was obviously the key to the whole problem. But when the day finally came for the white man to set forth in search of it the forest Indians must have invoked some powerful deity to protect their abode from the profanations of the intruder, so well kept appeared to be the secret of the elusive tree.

This day arrived in the year 1735, because a group of distinguished French scientists decided to measure the earth's meridian, for which purpose the French Government sent an expedition to the equatorial region of South America.

The three academicians, M. Godin, M. Bouguer, and M. de la Condamine, were the principal members of this famous expedition to which a botanist named Joseph de Jussieu was attached. The youngest of sixteen children, Joseph de Jussieu had been born at Lyon of noble lineage and, although he was a physician, he seemed to be following the family tradition since at the time of his voyage to the New World two of his brothers were already famous botanists and members of the Academy. In joining the expedition Jussieu's main purpose was to study the fever bark tree.

Of M. Godin, M. Bouguer, and M. de la Condamine a great deal is known, particularly of the latter two and mostly of M. de la Condamine. What brought these two scientists to the attention of the public was not so much their achievements, which concerned the abstruse sciences of mathematics and physics, but their disputes and professional rivalries which began when they took ship for the New World, were kept at a high peak while there, and were continued for many years after their return to France. Although M. Bouguer is considered to have been superior professionally to M. de la Condamine, the latter was a sophisticated opponent, a witty man of wider culture and interests and quick with his pen. He was, moreover, a worldly man of high birth, who corresponded with duchesses and was the intimate of statesmen. He had a gift for popularization and knew how to focus the attention of the public on his person and external charms more than on his questionable accomplishments. Thus, although he was only the third in command, the scientific mission to the Equator is known in history as La Condamine's Expedition. Bouguer, who was admittedly a great scientist and one devoid of any worldly gifts, hated him.

These men spent seven years of their lives together in an unknown country, without means of communication, traveling most of the time through the dismal jungles of South America. The obstacles to their task were almost insuperable. In order to make their measurements, their maps, and their astronomical observations they had to climb mountains, live in the most primitive conditions in all kinds of impossible climates, and travel enormous distances on foot; they were abandoned by their guides in inaccessible spots and their instruments were invariably lost, stolen, or damaged beyond repair; they had no money because funds promised by the French Government never arrived in time, if ever; they were sick and they were hungry. And during these seven years they never ceased betraying, slandering, and jeopardizing each other even at the risk of their lives.

The financial straits of the expedition were such that every member was forced to sell part of his personal belongings in order to support himself as best he could. These transactions were brought to the attention of the authorities of Quito, who took the French group to court on a criminal charge of carrying on illegal trade while traveling as guests of the Spanish Crown. The French scientists had no difficulty in acquitting themselves, with the exception of La Condamine, who at the time was absent in Lima and whose colleagues made no effort to vindicate him. Neither of them challenged or tried to clarify the statements of witnesses to the effect that he had sold small pieces of jewelry and had offered, for the same purpose, a number of fashionable "chemises" trimmed with lace, the purchase of which, however, no one in those parts dared to undertake. Regardless of how irritating La Condamine's personality was to his colleagues, their behavior was unforgivable, for he was reduced to the sale of his linen after having contributed large sums of his own money to the support of all members of the expedition. Fortunately for him, he was staying at this time as a personal guest in the palace of the Viceroy of Peru who, interfering promptly on his behalf, quickly put a stop to the ridiculous procedure against the French savant.

It was probably due to this ludicrous incident that the expedition was nicknamed the "French Company" by the local wits of Quito, who derived a great deal of personal enjoyment from the squabbles of the foreign scientists. In time the expedition became involved in several lawsuits with the natives, and the mobs eventually rioted against them with the purpose of carrying out a wholesale massacre. They satisfied themselves, however, with the murder, instigated by personal revenge, of M. de Seniergues, surgeon of the expedition, who had tried most unwisely to apply the solid principles of French logic to the solution of a local, complex, and passionate love affair. Thus ill-luck and continued misfortunes pursued the French expedition which carried in its midst a man who was searching for the fever bark tree.

In 1743, M. Bouguer returned to France, leaving M. de la Condamine in some forsaken spot in the wilderness, where he was making certain astronomical observations which M. Bouguer was supposedly checking from another strategic point. Two months and a half after Bouguer's departure La Condamine learned of it by accident. Thus he found that during all this time he had been carrying out completely valueless observations in the happy belief that his confrere was collaborating in the celestial measurements. Two years later, in 1745, M. de la Condamine himself went back to France. He had spent ten years in the New World, whereas he had expected to remain two or three at the most. He returned very much battered, completely deaf as the result of some accident, and full of infirmities, but always a quick and dangerous opponent to M. Bouguer. As for M. Godin, who was properly the official head of the expedition, he seemed to have kept very much to himself, little interested in all probability by the prevailing ill feelings and, adapting himself easily to the country and its people, became professor of astronomy in the University of San Marcos of Lima, where he remained for some time after his colleagues had returned to Europe.

Joseph de Jussieu, the botanist, remained in the New World. Nothing spectacular is known of him during the ten-year period spent by his colleagues in South America. In the voluminous literature concerning the expedition, particularly the diary of La Condamine, he is always somewhere in the background; he takes no side, quarrels with no one, either his colleagues or the natives, and his role seems to have been always that of the peacemaker and the healer, whether of body or soul, notwithstanding the fact that, in the light of subsequent events, he was probably the one who needed most the care and understanding which he so lavishly gave to others. Whatever happened, he kept to his work and shortly after his arrival was already in Loxa looking for the fever bark tree. But he had a competitor: none other than La Condamine himself. In 1737, La Condamine too was in Loxa and, after spending three days there, wrote a description of the tree which he immediately sent to the French Academy of Sciences, where it was read the following year. It was a great scientific event: the first eyewitness account of the famous fever bark tree. Shortly thereafter the description was sent to Karl von Linné, the great botanist of the time, who based upon it his classification of the tree, naming it genus *Cinchona*, in memory of the Countess of Chinchón. La Condamine's description, obviously the work of the layman, is a rather brief one and lacks details. In it he touches on all phases of the drug from an account of its discovery to the Indian etymology of the word "quinine." It is beautifully written and in spite of its inaccuracies clearly shows the wide learning of its author.

It seems obvious that in sending this report to Europe La
Condamine had intruded in the province of Jussieu, who
was the official botanist of the expedition. After this it would
not have been surprising if even the good-natured Jussieu
had hated him. Yet in his description La Condamine promised
the academicians that a far more learned treatise on the fever
bark tree was in store for them through the industry of M.
de Jussieu. Luck, however, pursued La Condamine in his
botanical venture as in everything else and, as the fates would
have it, his description of the fever bark tree became a classic
in the history of botany and the only authoritative source of
information for many years to come.

Though in the time of the Roman Empire Pliny the Elder
played the role of the fashionable scientist, Charles Marie de
la Condamine is probably the first example in contemporary
history of this particular type of scholar. Their role is not a
negligible one, for they are the great popularizers who arouse
general interest in the scientific enterprises of the day. The
real scientists scorn them, for they fail to realize their
ultimate dependence on the support of the great public for
the means to carry on their work.

On his return to France La Condamine, pursuing his new
botanical interests, took with him some young plants of the
fever bark tree with the intention of having them cultivated.
The trees, however, were lost during a violent storm at sea.
This was the first of a series of strange incidents which time
and again contrived to hinder the development of the new
remedy after the medical opposition against the drug had at
length been defeated. A new element had now come into
play, so subtle and elusive that it cannot fail to suggest to
the imagination what reason is forced to repudiate. Yet, as if

a malignant spell had been cast on the fever bark tree, every attempt to study it, every effort to acquaint the world with its properties, was doomed to failure and disaster. As if a curse followed those who touched the fever bark tree, Fate, availing itself of uncanny means, repeatedly threw its victims into the depths of strange misfortune and calamity, until the story of their stirring adventures reached the proportions of classical tragedy.

The first victim was Joseph de Jussieu. During the expedition he had spent several years in Loxa making a thorough study of the tree. He was the first to see its different species, which according to him were four: the red, the yellow, the white, and the gray. Of these La Condamine had vaguely described three, though admitting that he had never seen them. This difference in species accounted for the variations in the effectiveness of the barks. Jussieu also experimented with the extraction of the drug from the bark by different chemical procedures. He wrote down all his observations and prepared a detailed report in which he described minutely every species of the tree, the problems of its cultivation, and the best way of preparing the remedy. And he dwelt most particularly on the conservation of the miraculous forests, for, to his great amazement, the Indians chopped down the trees to strip them of their bark. Jussieu acquainted the natives with the properties of the various species of the fever bark tree so that only the most desirable would be sent to Europe. He also taught them how to prepare the drug for their own use since, incredible as it may seem, they claimed to be ignorant of its medicinal virtues although living in a malarial region. Jussieu's manuscript was a precious and unique document.

When his colleagues returned to France Jussieu had decided to remain in the New World, apparently to study the geographical distribution of the fever bark tree, toying probably with the idea of its possible cultivation. He traveled far and wide in the South American jungles and up and down the Andes Mountains in quest of the tree; in this pursuit he spent seventeen years. He was now without a sponsor and in order to support himself in his travelings he taught botany, practiced medicine, designed bridges and dams, and built roads. Besides the fever bark tree he studied an infinite number of plants as well as animals and minerals. He made maps and along with geographical descriptions studied the customs of the different Indian tribes. He accumulated an incredible amount of scientific material and put it carefully away in wooden boxes, which he never allowed out of his sight. There he kept his maps, manuscripts, and specimens of every description from the vegetable, mineral, and animal kingdoms. In those boxes he enclosed a whole new world which the scientists of his day had neither seen nor dreamed could exist.

Joseph de Jussieu had had for many years a servant who attended faithfully to his needs and who watched day and night over the mysterious boxes which, according to his master, contained objects of the greatest value. Finally Jussieu decided to return to France. On learning this the servant disappeared with the boxes in the belief that they held enough treasure for a king's ransom. They were never recovered.

This must have happened about 1761. Ten years passed, during which time nothing was known of the whereabouts of Jussieu; when he finally reached Paris in 1771 he was insane. He was sixty-seven years old, and a ghastly sight he must have been, appearing suddenly from a haunted world. He knew nothing and remembered nothing, but seemed to be the prey of great mental sufferings. Mercifully one of the older of his fifteen brothers was still alive to soothe him in his agony. What terrors persecuted him no one knew because he would not talk. For how long he had been insane and what calamities had befallen him no one could dare to guess. Perhaps after thirty-six years of wandering through the jungles his mind had succumbed to the panic fear which possesses the child of civilized man when thrown back to the point where the history of man began. He has no way of appeasing this paralyzing fear, which comes from within and has been handed down by those remote ancestors who, in primeval forests, fought the apocalyptic terrors of the past and whose image, vaguely engraved by a mysterious heritage in the dimmed recesses of the memory of man, is brought back to life in the forest.

Jussieu's tragedy, however, was reason enough for his madness, his mind in self-defense refusing to function when confronted with proof of the tragic helplessness of man, the outcome of whose life seems to be merely the result of accident. What amounted to the antics of a child had prevented Jussieu from becoming the great scientist of his age and had deprived the world of a scientific document which, in all probability, has never had its equal and which, as far as it concerned the fever bark tree, affected the lives of millions of people.

If anything, only a sense of deep humility could have saved Jussieu in his despair, a realization that before the great riddle of Providence and its relation to the destiny of man his mind was as unfitted to discern the light as that of his poor servant who, on opening the boxes, was confronted with the horrible realization that the white man's treasures were papers, dried bones, seeds, and stones.

In 1936, to commemorate the centenary of its foundation, a French industrial concern which manufactured quinine under the name Trois Cachets, published a manuscript by Jussieu. With one minor exception, it is the only work of his ever published; it is a description of the fever bark tree written originally in Latin and dated 1737, curiously enough the same year that La Condamine spent three days in Loxa and wrote his own description of the tree. Interspersed with Jussieu's Latin text are some notes written in Spanish by quite a different hand. In these notes Jussieu, assuming him to be the author, complains of fainting spells which overtook him on several occasions, all carefully dated up to the year 1778. On this late occasion he pretends somewhat weirdly to have fainted during his sleep, though he admits he was unaware of the accident. There is no way to explain these dates, unless he kept the manuscript in his possession after he was confined in an institution for the insane, from the year 1771 on, when he was apparently in no condition to write or to detect the passage of time, being constantly in a state of profound dejection. There is also no way of explaining the two handwritings. This manuscript was found in the Museum of Natural History in Paris. No explanation has been offered as to how it got there or why it was not published before, although it is far more documented than La Condamine's description. Like everything else connected with Jussieu, this manuscript has a quality of mystery which leaves the reader with an indefinable desire to know more about that which, in all probability, was buried forever in Jussieu's tortured mind.

Joseph de Jussieu died on April 11, 1779, in terrible agonies of mental suffering. And the world at large knew nothing of the fever bark tree.

CHAPTER VII

The Botanical Institute of the
New Kingdom of Granada

For centuries after Columbus's fateful voyage in 1492 a number of Spanish young men each year felt the urge to go to the New World. Most of them did go and in the course of time managed to acquire a very unsavory reputation. Although some of them, perhaps many, were indeed soldiers of fortune, captains of industry, and fanatic men of God, it eventually became clear that their bad reputation had been greatly enhanced by a peculiar tendency to emphasize their wicked deeds, whereas whatever may have been virtuous or commendable about them was systematically ignored. This tendency, methodically pursued, crystallized into the "Black Legend" of vague origin which sings of the viciousness and unspeakable cruelties of the Spanish conquistadors. Now and again on various occasions efforts have been made by impartial observers, most scholars, to dilute the deep black of the Spanish legend. Nevertheless their efforts will be of no avail. Legends have a greater appeal to the imagination than actual facts, and no one cares to have the wild, plundering Spaniards of the past changed into able administrators, efficient missionaries, and honest merchants, deserving but dull, thus depriving the peoples of more sober nations of the pleasure of indulging their fancies in the fantastic saga of the fierce conquistadors, objectionable but irresistibly alluring.

In the year 1757 a young man had traveled from Cadiz in

the south of Spain to Madrid with the intention of finding an opportunity to go to the New World. His name was José Celestino Mutis, he was twenty-five years old, and he had just graduated from medical school. Opportunity, however, did not seem to come his way, and young Mutis languished in despair for some time. Meanwhile he practiced medicine and studied mathematics, philosophy, and natural history so successfully that he was chosen by the King of Spain to be sent with other students to the great universities of Paris, Leyden, and Bohemia. Mutis, however, declined the honor because he wanted to go only to the New World. Yet it seemed quite obvious that he was not eager for the riches of the new continent, nor for a political career; neither was he an adventurous youth, but lived in scholarly retirement, devoting himself to his studies. Nor, finally, was he possessed by the mystical urge to convert the heathen Indian nations to Christianity, although he was a most devout Catholic. In fact his eyes were directed not toward the heavenly spheres but were constantly glued to the ground. Wherever he wandered, whether through fields or meadows or the streets of Madrid, he was constantly stooping down to pick up an herb, a bit of grass, or anything that grew from the soil, and in the contemplation of these humble objects he would become happily oblivious of the world around him. Mutis was a born naturalist, and that is why he wanted so much to go to the New World.

Cadiz in the eighteenth century had become the port of the Indies, the port of Seville having gradually been filled by the sands. Thus Mutis, like Cardinal de Lugo, had during his youth watched the arrival of Spanish galleons from the Indies. And, like Cardinal de Lugo, he had seen that besides gold, silver, and precious stones they were also loaded with exotic plants and animals. He must have listened to the sailors' tales about the natural wonders of the New World and longed for the sight of them with an all-consuming desire. His chance finally came in 1760, when there was a change of viceroys in the New Kingdom of Granada (the Colombia of today), named after one of Spain's most beautiful cities. A new viceroy always took with him his own retinue and Mutis asked for a position as botanist with financial support from the Crown to carry on his studies. He pointed out the great advantages of his project, which was to begin with a systematic study of the cinchona forests, on which hinged the problem of the production and distribution of quinine, so important for the welfare of mankind. The viceroy, Marqués de la Vega de Armijo, agreed to the undertaking and warmly praised Mutis's plans as most laudable and commendable. Nevertheless he thought it better not to disturb the king with such irrelevant matters, burdened as he was at the moment with the cares of state, and suggested that Mutis be attached to his household as his private physician. The important thing for Mutis, suggested the viceroy, was to get to America and, once there, means would be found to give him the necessary support so that he could begin his study of the cinchona trees.

On February 12, 1761, the new viceroy made his official entrance into Santa Fé de Bogotá, the capital of the New Kingdom of Granada. Mutis had scarcely unpacked his bags when, with the buoyancy of youth, he sat down to write a letter to the "Prince of Naturalists," the Swedish botanist Karl von Linné, whose new system for the classification of plants had brought about revolutionary changes and who was the most eminent man of his time. In his letter Mutis told the great man (who had never heard of him) of his trip to America and of plans for work, which envisaged no less than a natural history of the new continent, preparing him for the arrival in the very near future of unique collections of the rarest plants. Linné, whether touched by the enthusiasm of his young correspondent or because he had remained generous in his greatness, answered Mutis immediately. In his letter he treated him as an already illustrious colleague, gave him encouragement and advice, requested his help, thanked him warmly for the forthcoming collections of plants, and acquainted him with the good news that he had made him a member of the Academy of Sciences of Upsala. Thus began a correspondence that was to last until Linné's death seventeen years later.

Unfortunately the viceroy, who had courteously agreed to the significance of Mutis's projects, did not in practice really share his enthusiasms for the natural sciences. After their arrival he ignored the issue and, forgetting Mutis's previous requests, praised him warmly as an excellent physician of whose services he could not be deprived. The aristocracy of Bogotá also flocked to his door and Mutis soon became a busy, fashionable practitioner. When he realized what had happened to him he was in despair, and five months after his arrival in Bogotá he wrote in his diary: "While in Spain I believed that by now I should already be on my way to Loxa to study the cinchona tree . . . so assuredly the viceroy had promised me that shortly after our arrival here he would send me on this errand." Mutis longed for the cinchona tree, but it obviously was not an object of great importance to the forgetful viceroy.

Having no means by which he could support himself unless the viceroy gave him the promised help, Mutis had to continue with the practice of medicine, unable to limit the number of his patients lest he hurt the feelings of the local aristocracy.

He made heroic efforts to give a little time to botany, and on his way from delivering a baby or attending a case of malaria he would stoop down constantly in the streets of Bogotá to pick up a bit of grass or a flower, which he carefully cherished and took home but never seemed to find time to examine carefully. Having exhausted the urban flora, he took to observing birds, insects, reptiles, and minerals, and sent to Linné the descriptions of any specimen not known in Europe. The urban fauna, however, were also limited; Mutis was miserable, and life in the court became so unbearable that he refused to attend any official ceremony because, he wrote, "I want to avoid the bitterness which always comes from human relationships." Finally, to ease his mind of the hated routine, he began to teach mathematics in the university according to the precepts of Newton, and thus became one of the first to bring the Newtonian philosophy to the New World. This aroused the anger of the Dominicans, who denounced Mutis to the Inquisition as a dubious Catholic in a futile attempt to revive opposition against the Copernican system. But Mutis answered the Dominicans with a brilliant dissertation showing the soundness of the Copernican system as demonstrated by the experiments of Galileo, Kepler, and Newton. This dissertation he presented to the Inquisition itself, of which he had no fear even though meanwhile he himself had become a priest. Mutis was deeply religious, yet in taking orders he was probably seeking escape from worldly contacts which were so painful to his nature.

Time went by and Mutis continued to be miserable. He had not come to America to practice medicine or to teach mathematics, much less to argue with the Dominicans upon astronomical laws. He had come to study the natural riches of the

New World and, forgetting the proper demeanor of courtiers, he must have annoyed the viceroy with frequent and ill-timed reminders of his promise, for the viceroy did what high officials usually do on such uncomfortable occasions: he passed the responsibility on to a still higher official. On his advice Mutis presented a petition to the king in 1763, suggesting the formation of a botanical expedition. It is a pathetic document. He pointed out to the king that Spain was neglecting the study of the natural sciences, in which other countries were making extraordinary progress, and emphasized that Spain should have the best museum of natural history in the world. He reminded the king that already his forebears had recognized the importance of the task, and thus Philip II and Ferdinand VI had sent scientists to America for this purpose. Without comment he mentioned the attempts already made by foreign nations to study the natural resources of the New World. The work, however, was far from done and thus destiny had reserved for the most glorious of all kings this magnificent enterprise, the completion of the natural history of America, for which the scientific world was so eager.

After a certain amount of flattery he courteously but firmly emphasized Spain's duty to the world in having been awarded by Providence such enormous possessions. "America," he said, "is not only rich in gold, silver, precious stones and other treasures but also in natural products of the greatest value. . . . There is quinine, a priceless possession of which Your Majesty is the only owner and which divine Providence has bestowed upon you for the good of mankind. It is indispensable to study the cinchona tree so that only the best kind will be sold to the public at the lowest price." He further described to the king the tragic situation of a physician watching the death of a destitute patient who had spent his last pennies on a worthless remedy. He warned that if the usual procedure of chopping down the trees to get the bark was continued the supply of the drug would become exhausted in a short time. And, availing himself of the use of metaphor, he threatened the king with punishment from above by describing the spectacle of him seated on his throne surrounded by the ghosts of those who had died for lack of the remedy, thus laying their deaths on his conscience. With a prophetic touch he quoted the example of the Dutch who attended so efficiently to the production and distribution of their cinnamon from the East Indies, although it had no bearing on the welfare of mankind.

He finally asked for a minimum of support to carry out the formidable enterprise of preparing a natural history of America and, while making an effort not to frighten the king with grand projects, his imagination running wild, he speculated on how from this study the sciences of medicine, geography, astronomy, and mathematics would derive great benefits. This petition, of considerable length, was accompanied by a few lines from the viceroy formally recommending the project, which he still considered a most laudable and commendable enterprise.

No answer came from the Crown. A year later, in 1764, Mutis sent another petition, and again no answer came. In the same year he sent to Linné some specimens from the cinchona tree which had been presented to him by the superintendent of the cinchona forest in Loxa. Linné was most grateful to Mutis for these examples which allowed him to complete his classification of the tree. "I was delighted," he wrote, "with the beautiful drawing of the bark and the leaves and flowers that you sent me, which flowers . . . gave me a clear impression of a very rare species, quite different from the one I had formed from the drawings of M. de la Condamine. . . ." Twenty-five years had thus elapsed from the time La Condamine's description of the fever bark tree had been read in Paris until the foremost botanist of the time was able to secure direct information bearing on the plant which concerned the world-wide problem of malaria.

Exportation of the bark was now in the hands of the Spanish Government, although this fact put no restrictions on any private individual or enterprise, whether Spanish or foreign, to trade with it. The government had its own superintendent, who managed the collecting of the bark but who unfortunately was not a botanical expert. Notwithstanding, the man who gave Mutis the specimen which he sent to Linné had become well acquainted with the cinchona tree after years of wandering through the forests of Loxa. He told Mutis that he had seen the cinchona growing in the region of the New Kingdom of Granada, a fact strengthened by local accounts, according to which Joseph de Jussieu, who had traveled extensively through that country, had been the first to discover these particular cinchonas. If true, this meant that the tree could survive north of the Equator. The range of its geographical distribution thus was fabulous, because it would extend from the Atlantic to the Pacific, thereby simplifying the problem of its transportation in one unforeseen manner, for previously every ounce of bark which had gone to Europe had been carried around Cape Horn.

All this set Mutis on fire; again he went to the viceroy, who once more acknowledged the importance of the botanical study of the tree but repeated that there was nothing he could do about it since the Crown had ignored Mutis's petition. As a final concession he gave his harassed physician permission to take an occasional day away from his duties in order to explore the outskirts of the city of Bogotá in search of the cinchona tree. And so Mutis went out on pathetic journeys to look for the tree, an almost hopeless task because he had never seen one. It was a matter of long practice to distinguish the inconspicuous trunk of the cinchonas from the infinite variety of other trees, a task further complicated by the differences between the several species of cinchonas themselves and by the fact that, in the thickness of the South American forests, the foliage of trees cannot be perceived from the ground.

On these excursions he collected some unknown plants which he sent to Linné as a meager token of the magnificent collections he had offered the Swedish botanist and which had seemed so real during the first glorious days after his arrival in the New World. Linné continued to write encouragingly, mentioned him profusely in his scientific papers, and named one of the most beautiful flowering plants after him. But Mutis was miserable, and he was ill of intense fatigue, mental as well as physical. He was also financially ruined because he had spent large sums of money attempting to grow rare plants in his garden and making collections of specimens, and because he had neglected his patients to wander aimlessly through the forests, like a man possessed, in search of a tree.

In 1766, five years after his arrival in America, unable any longer to stand life in the capital, or more probably the sight of the viceroy, Mutis suddenly became interested in the problems of mining and left Bogotá to settle in a dilapidated silver mine located in one of the most desolate spots of creation. There he lived for four years in a shack under the most primitive conditions while he immersed himself in the study of the extraction of ores, labor conditions, and everything else relating to the mines.

In 1770 he returned to Bogotá for no known reason unless he had been informed of an impending change of viceroys or had exhausted the flora and fauna of his immediate surroundings. Again he practiced medicine, which he also taught, following the principles of Boerhaave, one of the foremost clinicians of modern medicine; and again he taught Newton's theory of gravity; he also expounded botany according to the new system devised by Linné. Thus he was an early protagonist in the New World of three of the most important scientific advances of the time.

Mutis's versatility in all branches of learning was phenomenal. Some years later the King of Spain received an unusual request from Catherine II, Empress of Russia, asking him for any grammars or dictionaries of the Indian languages. Catherine's request was forwarded to the viceroys and it was learned that Mutis had been collecting all works of this kind through a complex correspondence with missionaries scattered throughout the continent. Copies of the works in Mutis's possession were sent to Catherine and the originals he kept as precious relics to be delivered to some institution of learning because, he wrote, "suspecting how quickly these tongues are passing into oblivion . . . and foreseeing that these unique antiquities will become an object of the greatest curiosity, it would cause bitter disappointment not to find trace of them or even to be able to ascertain whether they had ever existed."

By now the youth of Bogotá had begun to feel Mutis's influence and a group of brilliant and enthusiastic young men gathered around him, eager to learn the new philosophies. From their number Mutis chose one named Clemente Ruiz, whom he sent to Sweden in 1773 to become a mining engineer in order to carry out some reforms he had planned for the mining industry. Mutis paid Ruiz's expenses and supported him for four years in Sweden. With him he sent to Linné a precious bundle which contained the dry leaves and flowers of the new *Cinchona bogotensis* which Mutis had found at last in the forests of the New Kingdom of Granada, by accident of sheer luck. One day while traveling from his mine to Bogotá he had happened to look out over the mountain slopes from a ridge and there under his eyes had been the new cinchonas, unmistakable this time, for they were in full bloom.

This discovery of the *Cinchona bogotensis* in the New Kingdom of Granada offered final proof that the tree grew all the way from the Atlantic to the Pacific. Now once it could be found to grow north of the Equator, there would be no limit to the range of its geographical distribution, and in fact it did not take very long to find out that the tree grew practically all over South America. Consequently in no time the bark could be had in almost every port on the east coast, and large quantities of it were soon smuggled into England and the United States, where it was sold at fantastic prices. Thus it was not until 1772 that the real mass trade in quinine began, almost one hundred and fifty years after its discovery. This prompted the new viceroy of the New Kingdom to send a report to the king, in 1773, suggesting the formation of a quinine monopoly to save the drug from being the subject of speculation by unscrupulous merchants. Should the Crown have the monopoly, the drug could be sold at a low price and its supply organized in such a way that the quinine of Peru could be exported to the Philippines and the Orient, whereas that of the New Kingdom could be exported to

Europe. A voluminous correspondence ensued between Spain and the high officials in South America but no definite results came of it. Considering the different species of the tree, its variations in the content of quinine, and the enormous and inaccessible range of its distribution, the first step in organizing a state monopoly was obviously to make a thorough botanical study of the tree, with a view to its possible cultivation, as Mutis had proposed. Yet both he and his projects were completely ignored.

In 1776 there was again a change in viceroys and Mutis went out to greet the new incumbent while he was on his way to the capital. Whatever expectations of help he may have had from the new viceroy must have quickly vanished because a year later, in 1777, on the return of Ruiz from Sweden, Mutis, forsaking his academic activities in Bogotá, left with the new engineer for another silver mine. He was still there five years later when again a new viceroy came to the New Kingdom of Granada (one other intermediate appointee meanwhile having fallen victim of malaria and died on his way up the river to the capital of New Granada even before he had actually taken over his duties).

Mutis, who was now fifty years old, must have given up all hope of ever attaining his scientific ambition because he made no attempt to present his respects. In this case, however, although Mutis did not go to the mountain, the mountain came to Mutis, for Antonio Caballero Góngora, who happened to be an archbishop as well as a viceroy, in 1782 paid his pastoral visit to the remote spot where Mutis lived in his mine. Góngora was a scholar and a patron of science, and his astonishment was limitless at finding José Mutis lost in the wilderness of the New World. When Mutis told him the sad story of his coming to America and of his failures, the archbishop's astonishment turned to fury. Then and there he took Mutis with him to his palace in Bogotá and immediately began to deluge the authorities in Madrid, from the king down, with all kinds of petitions, reports, and recommendations to the effect that a botanical expedition should be organized in the New Kingdom of Granada under the direction of the great scientist José Mutis. If anything further was needed to arouse the archbishop, it was the news that the King of Spain had granted special permission to the German naturalist, Baron von Humboldt, to explore the Americas in order to study their natural riches. That was too much for the sanguine archbishop and without waiting for a reply from Spain he organized a provisional scientific commission entitled "The Botanical Expedition of the New Kingdom of Granada," composed of Mutis as director, an assistant, and one painter, because Mutis considered the written description of plants most inadequate.

Such was the archbishop's dogged persistence that finally Charles III, King of Spain, in November 1783, made Mutis by royal decree the chief botanist and astronomer of the botanical expedition. By order of the Crown his debts were paid and he was awarded a pension of two thousand pesos a year to continue his studies. Moreover orders were given that all the instruments and books necessary for the expedition should be bought in England on behalf of the Crown. The first thing the expedition did was to send botanists to explore the forests in search of the cinchona tree. The most efficient of these botanists was a Franciscan priest named Diego Garcia, who found the tree in the most unexpected locations and who for several years continued his explorations, discovering a large number of plants, some of medicinal value. Father Garcia sent several manuscripts to the Museum of Natural History in Madrid, describing a large number of plants and animals; they have never been published and they may be of the greatest value.

The staff of the expedition settled in a tiny town called Mariquita, strategically located at the edge of the jungle, and there Mutis gave himself up to an orgy of botany. He at last began a real botanical garden and made the first attempt to cultivate the cinchona tree, starting a plantation which must have thrived for a considerable period of time, because Von Humboldt saw the remains of it some fifteen years later. By 1787 Mutis had several assistants, field workers, and five artists purposely sent from Quito, whose painters had a reputation for dexterity. He put in order all the materials he had collected over the years of his pilgrimages and thus the expedition started a library unique of its kind. The time finally arrived when he could have sent Linné those priceless collections of plants he had offered him twenty-six years before; but the Swedish naturalist had died nine years previously. To the end he had encouraged his young friend, continued to mention him in his writings, praised his achievements to his colleagues all over Europe, and finally bestowed upon him the title of "Prince of American Naturalists."

In no time the expedition began to accumulate manuscripts, specimens, and above all an endless number of hand-painted illustrations. The artists from Quito, like medieval monks, worked nine hours a day in complete silence. The drawings were in natural size and done in the utmost detail, showing all phases of the plants' growth, including the seeds and the roots. In order to obtain an exact replica of the plants Mutis devised means for preparing dyes from natural sources so that the colors would be exact duplicates of the originals. Apart from their scientific value, these illustrations were magnificent works of art, more dear to Mutis than any conceivable treasure. Responsibility for protecting them kept him in continuous agony because of the pernicious habit of the inhabitants of Mariquita, who every Saturday had a major fiesta which they properly celebrated by setting off abundant quantities of firecrackers. On these occasions Mutis, like the traditional witch, perched himself on the roof of the expedition's house, brandishing a broom to sweep away the falling live ashes and thus avoid an otherwise inevitable fire. In an attempt to compensate for the lost years he worked so hard and so tensely at a great variety of problems that he fell ill. The government in Bogotá, aware of the value of the material collected by the expedition, ordered it moved to the capital for fear that, should Mutis die, the house might be looted or burned, since anything could be expected from the merrymaking citizens of Mariquita.

The order was carried out in 1791, and although the viceroy-archbishop had left two years before, the new viceroy continued to protect the expedition with the same enthusiasm his predecessor had shown. The expedition was housed in excellent quarters with an enormous library and all kinds of scientific instruments, and became the Botanical Institute of the New Kingdom of Granada. The staff now consisted of some ten scientists and fourteen artists. In order to have a staff of the latter always on hand, Mutis made provision that all children of the orphanage of Bogotá, who showed any inclination and ability for botanical drawing, should be trained in this art in order to join the institute with full-time salary at the end of their schooling. A large number of volunteers from the intellectual youth of Bogotá who had studied under Mutis and who were imbued by the new scientific concepts also joined the institute. Among these there was a particularly brilliant man named Francisco José de Caldas. The institute became the center of Bogotá's intellectual life. Chiefly through Mutis's correspondence with Linné's son, who had continued his father's work and also his father's partiality for him, it was known in all the academic centers of Europe as a unique organization from which extraordinary things were to be expected. Up to 1793, however, nothing had been published by the Botanical Institute. Material was being constantly accumulated and everyone was busy arranging the two major works in progress: a monumental treatise on the flora of the septentrional zone, which included thousands of illustrations, and a complete medical and botanical treatise on the cinchona tree, also profusely illustrated. Yet somehow or other the work was never ready for the printer.

By now the Spanish Government was really intent on the study of the natural products of America, particularly the cinchonas. Even before the Botanical Institute had been established two botanists, Ruiz and Pavón, accompanied by the French naturalist, Dombey, and two assistants, had been sent on a scientific mission to Peru in 1777. For eleven years they explored Peru and Chile and gathered together an enormous collection of specimens, mostly of the cinchonas. But ill luck dogged their efforts. Their manuscripts were destroyed by a fire in Peru; and the *San Pedro de Alcántara*, on which the fifty cases of specimens were being transported to Spain, was "shipwrecked." In spite of these calamities the two collaborators managed to publish in 1792 some information on the cinchona and an excellent flora of Peru and Chile. Much later, in 1852, their years of careful work were revealed when their magnificent collection of bark specimens was found in the British Museum, the bulk of which had originally been sold at auction in the city of London as part of the cargo of a Spanish prize. All of which seems to suggest that the shipwreck in which Ruiz's and Pavón's botanical collection was lost had not been a shipwreck at all.

It was probably because of the loss of this scientific material that the Spanish Government gave orders in 1793 for an investigation to be carried out at the Botanical Institute of the New Kingdom of Granada, in order to discover the reasons why publication of the important studies was delayed. The results were far from encouraging, for the report stated that, although the material already gathered was priceless and limitless, the time of publication was extremely doubtful because there was not a single manuscript in order or near it, only thousands of illustrations, thousands of botanical descriptions, all scattered in utter confusion as by the hand of a mad spirit.

The mad spirit was Mutis himself. Throughout his life it was obvious that he was a misanthrope, not as in the original sense of the word one who hates mankind but in the modern sense which conveys the idea of one who fears mankind. He refused in his youth to attend the official functions in the viceroy's palace in order to avoid "the bitterness that always comes from human relationships." When unable to follow his inclinations he reluctantly took to the teaching of mathematics, natural history, and medicine as an intellectual escape. Of all his activities, however, the one he really hated was the practice of medicine, which put him face to face with the miseries of mankind. His choice of mining problems was no doubt the result of his desire for complete solitude. When his greatest wish in life was granted he chose a hidden corner of the earth in which to do his work, and a government order was required to force him to move to Bogotá. With age, disappointment, and disease this morbid tendency was probably increased.

When at the age of sixty-one he was confronted with the necessity of exposing to public scrutiny, which he so greatly dreaded, the most important part of himself—the fruits of his passionate love for the prodigy of nature, born through so much sorrow and pain—he simply could not endure it. The most insignificant flower of the field, the commonest of all the shrubs was to Mutis a unique wonder, the living proof of the miraculous harmony prevailing in the humblest work of the Creator. After a lifelong, bitter struggle he had taken indescribable pains to have these wonders reproduced with such meticulous exactitude that the illustrations were as much a wonder as the originals themselves. To have these perfect works of art and scientific achievement thrown into the market place to be looked at with indifference by the eyes of the profane was an unbearable thought to Mutis. Nevertheless he finally published two short pamphlets on the cinchona tree in the years 1792 and 1793, either to placate the government or from a sense of duty. Both dealt with medical problems relating to the administration of the drug, and although in the latter he described four species of the tree, thus adding one more to the three listed by La Condamine, there was little detail as to their botanical features.

When one realizes that these papers by Mutis were the first to deal with the cinchona tree since La Condamine's description had been read in Paris fifty-five years before, his emphasis on the medical properties of the bark was a rather irrelevant if not an exasperating one. It was obvious that after Talbor had found the method for its administration and Torti had published his exhaustive clinical study on the action of the drug on malaria, the medical profession could make no further advance with the new remedy until it had become a standard product. Physicians had been waiting patiently for the last hundred years for the botanist to bring about this event, and whatever medical studies had been carried out in the meantime clearly showed the prevailing confusion concerning the properties of the drug. Some physicians favored the red bark while others recommended the yellow and still others the white; they also argued over what locality produced the best kind of bark. Meanwhile La Condamine's description was their only botanical authority in addition to the meager results of their experience; they did not know that the same kind of bark, whether red, yellow, or white, whether from Peru or from the New Kingdom, might contain a great deal of the drug or none at all. At the end of the eighteenth century the first trials were made by chemists to analyze the bark in a fruitless attempt to solve the riddle of its erratic behavior.

The year 1801 arrived, the nineteenth century began, and quinine was still as elusive an entity as it had been one hundred and fifty years ago at the time of its discovery. But in the Botanical Institute of the New Kingdom of Granada a colossal treatise on the cinchona tree was slowly taking shape. More and more illustrations, descriptions, and observations were added to it; but what was going to make it a unique piece of work was the contribution of Francisco José de Caldas, who had joined the institute years before as a voluntary worker and who had become one of its outstanding members. He made a diagram of the complete geographical distribution of the different varieties of the cinchona tree, including the conditions attending their growth: climate, altitude, moisture, sunshine, and the like. This work was included in a detailed botanical map of the Andes on which Caldas was working at a feverish speed.

In 1801 Mutis was sixty-nine years old. He was a decrepit, sick man, almost totally blind, and in all probability a very difficult person to deal with. In this year, however, there occurred in his life a great event which led to the only public acknowledgment ever bestowed on him but one which was probably a fair compensation for all the labors of his life. Baron von Humboldt had finally undertaken his projected trip to the New World, accompanied by the French naturalist Bonpland. Their objective was Peru, where Von Humboldt wanted to see the cinchona tree, and they planned, after landing on the Atlantic coast, to cross the narrow strip of Panama to take ship in the Pacific to Guayaquil. Making an appalling detour, however, which included forty-five days of navigation up the Magdalena River, they went first to Bogotá with the purpose, as stated by Von Humboldt, of "seeing the famous Mutis."

The two scientists examined the material gathered in the institute, illustration by illustration and description by description, and on their return to Europe they repeatedly stated that they had never seen anything like it. And indeed they never had, for the collection they had examined was truly unique. The Botanical Institute of the New Kingdom of Granada was, in fact, the first institution for pure scientific research in the Western world: the dream of every scientist since the history of science began and the like of which was not duplicated until the twentieth century, when the age of science really came into being. At the time of Von Humboldt's visit there were thirty artists working full time in the institute, with a scientific staff of about fifteen people, all extremely competent and all enjoying generous salaries. The library was described by Von Humboldt as the richest in the world in the sphere of natural history. He bestowed the greatest praise on Caldas's achievements, both in this field and in that of mathematics, for he had discovered how to measure altitude with the thermometer, succeeding with the very delicate instruments he himself had constructed for his experiments. This discovery was, incidentally, of the greatest importance in determining the range of altitude in which the different cinchonas grew.

In view of the complexity of the tasks carried out at the institute, Von Humboldt stated that only an exceptional man like Mutis could be capable of planning and directing them. So great in fact was the boundless admiration of Von Humboldt and Bonpland for Mutis that, on publishing a treatise on the "equinoxial plants" as a result of their trip, they caused to be made a beautiful engraving of Mutis's portrait which they placed on the front page, as a "humble token" of their respect and recognition. Baron von Humboldt was considered by many as the greatest European scientist of his time. His deferential recognition of Mutis should confirm the latter as the greatest American scientist of his day.

Mutis's influence on the history of Spanish America is of vital importance and deserves far more consideration than it has heretofore been given. A "Patriotic Society" of which he became the first president was founded in Bogotá for the purpose of improving the agriculture, commerce, industry, practical sciences, liberal arts, and internal policies of the New Kingdom of Granada. The nucleus of the society was centered in the men who in their youth had been Mutis's students and who had learned from him the medicine of Boerhaave, the mathematics of Newton, and the natural history of Linné. They were artists, geographers, naturalists, astronomers, mathematicians, physicians, and industrialists. They were Spanish, mestizos, and Indians, and they formed one of the most brilliant groups that has ever graced the life of a nation. And when they gathered together in the Patriotic Society they laid the foundations for the independence of a continent and Spain's loss of her American colonies.

In 1803, although an invalid, full of ailments, and completely blind, Mutis obtained financial support for the construction in Bogotá of the first astronomical observatory in South America. And there, as a memorial to a heroic and pathetic story, was hung a pendulum from the equipment of the so-called La Condamine Expedition, a relic found somewhere in Ecuador, where it had been lost or forgotten by a group of very harassed though somewhat formidable men of science.

José Celestino Mutis died in 1808 at the age of seventy-six without publishing a word of the colossal mass of illustrations and manuscripts he had accumulated and which he left in such a state of unbelievable confusion that only a sadistic hand, purposely and deliberately, could have performed the task. Caldas became one of the directors of the institute and, on orders from Madrid, immediately set about arranging the work of Mutis for publication, beginning with the treatise on the cinchona tree which included his own work. Caldas, however, was not able to devote himself for very long to the preparation of this great work. Two years after Mutis's death a general insurrection against the Spanish Government took place in the New Kingdom of Granada. Caldas, and with him all the members of the institute, joined in the rebellion, which had a successful outcome.

By 1811 a provisional government was instituted, the Botanical Institute resumed its normal course, and Caldas was ordered to prepare Mutis's work for the printer. The Spanish forces, however, were still fighting in the north and a year later Caldas was more or less forced to leave the institute, to become a captain of engineers. Sent to the north, incongruously enough, he took his instruments with him, to continue his work while fighting the Spaniards. He was a soldier now but, skeptical as to the glories of war, he wrote from the battlefield to a colleague in Bogotá: "Save from ultimate destruction the instruments of the observatory. . . . Do it as a service to posterity and devote yourself to the science of Cassini, Kepler, Copernicus and Newton; continue what I began and maintain the honor of this establishment, which will do for the glory of our country far more than all these armies and uniforms. . . ."

Nevertheless he was a great patriot and, though longing for his work, he helped the cause of his country's independence by building cannons, gunpowder mills, ammunition factories, and fortifications. In the midst of the prevailing disorder he managed to organize an academy of engineers, and in the opening lecture he quoted Fénelon and analyzed the nature of true patriotism. This subject was no doubt very dear to his heart, because the internal strifes and treacheries which were to annihilate Bolivar's plan of making the Great Colombia, the federation of the United States of South America, were already hindering the original rebellion itself. In fact the internal dissensions so weakened the revolutionary forces that in 1816 the Spanish armies succeeded in invading the New

Kingdom of Granada from Venezuela. One of the Spanish leaders had promised total amnesty if the New Kingdom would return to the Crown. The civil wars and political calamities endured by the people during their five years of independence had been such that they cheered the Spaniards when the latter entered Bogotá. For a while it looked as if the rebellion had failed but a Spanish general, disregarding the promise solemnly given in the name of the King of Spain, decided on a thorough repression of the rebels and terror spread throughout the New Kingdom of Granada.

Caldas was arrested and condemned to death. When the sentence was passed he had nothing to say in his defense. He addressed the Court, however, to remind them of something more precious than his or any man's life: the work accumulated in the Botanical Institute including the study of the cinchona tree on which depended the lives of millions of people all over the world. Mutis's work would be of no value to anyone since he, Caldas, was the only person who could put it in order. Three years before his death Mutis had asked Caldas to abandon his field work in the Andes and remain with him until he should die. During these three years Mutis made a valiant effort to bring order out of chaos, devoted himself to explaining to his pupil the plans of his work, uncovering to him the perfect coherence of his manuscripts, carefully disguised under their apparent disorder, a disorder intended to conceal some secret discoveries that Mutis claimed to have made, but which were probably a figment of his imagination resulting from his peculiar state of mind.

Caldas therefore was in a position to publish Mutis's work, together with his own, in a relatively short period of time, and he asked the Court that this time be granted him before the death sentence was executed. His request was denied. He sent a written petition to the authorities, stating the case in full detail and giving a list of his works which included, in addition to the geographical distribution of the cinchona trees, the measurements of altitude by the thermometer, the laws governing the atmospheric tides, the temperature of the valleys, a complete botanical map of the Andes, the distribution of their perpetual snows and their geological formation. His request was again denied.

On the eve of his execution he was asked to give further details concerning his work and that of Mutis with a view to their possible publication. Once again he asked for a postponement of the death sentence: only six months, and he would work with a chain tied to his ankle if necessary. Again it was denied him. All hope lost, he delivered to his jailer a finished manuscript of astronomical observations with final instructions for its publication. The next day, October 29, 1816, Francisco José de Caldas was executed with his back turned to the firing squad, as traitors must die. And that was the end of the Botanical Institute of the New Kingdom of Granada; all Caldas's colleagues were either executed or driven into exile.

Bolivar's forces, however, were threatening Bogotá and a year later, by orders from Madrid, all the scientific material in the Botanical Institute was taken to Spain. And thirty artists, mostly from Quito, lost their jobs; imperturbably, like medieval monks, the story goes, they had kept to their tasks, painting nine hours a day in absolute silence. Wholly immersed in the undertaking of transferring to canvas, stroke by stroke, the whole world of nature, they had been quite unaware that around them the terrors of war and revolution were sweeping throughout the land of the New Kingdom of Granada. So it should not be surprising to learn that, of the one hundred and four large wooden boxes taken to Spain, fourteen contained 5190 colored illustrations and 711 drawings, while two other boxes were filled with colored illustrations of animals and other subjects. Of the rest, forty-eight contained botanical specimens, mostly of the cinchona tree, and a large number of manuscripts, among which was included Mutis's *Herbarium*, gathered throughout all the years he had spent in America, and in which were described and catalogued more than twenty thousand plants. In the course of time these boxes were deposited in the cellars of the Botanical Institute of Madrid and most of them have never been opened. The Spanish Government, which spent untold sums of money in the Botanical Institute, has never been able to spare the money to publish these unique records of scientific achievement.

There were two copies of Mutis's treatise on the cinchona tree. In 1818 a botanist named La Gasca was asked to arrange for publication one of the copies, which he took with him to his home in Cadiz, Mutis's own home town. This treatise included 122 colored illustrations of the cinchona tree and yet was a rather modest effort considering that Caldas's monumental work on the tree was excluded. A local revolt broke out in Cadiz a few months later, and La Gasca's house was looted; all the manuscripts in his possession were destroyed, including Mutis's work. And the world still knew nothing of the fever bark tree.

CHAPTER VIII

The Breaking of the Spell

More than two thousand years had gone by since Alexander the Great died in India. Many things had happened in those years; his part of the world had changed beyond recognition. The Greek culture he so greatly admired and which he wanted to expand toward the Orient, where he believed the center of the future world would be, had shifted instead toward the Occident, escaping from the fevers that had killed him. New nations had been born, and although the light of the Alexandrine legend still shone unrivaled, a galaxy of resplendent names had filled the books of history.

Yet, had Alexander been reborn at the beginning of the nineteenth century, he would have detected little change in the external factors by which the life of men is conditioned. As in his time, the horse and the sailboat were the chief means of locomotion; the same ancestral tools of his Macedonian peasants were used in agriculture; slavery and forced labor, as in his day, were the basis of production. The principal changes belonged mainly to the domain of ideas, for to put ideas into practice man had first to master the natural forces about him, of which disease had proved so far the most rebellious and was thus the great obstacle to the expansion of trade and agriculture and to the formidable Industrial Revolution that was in the making.

Medicine had advanced but little since the time of Alexander, even in the domain of ideas, and he would have recognized without difficulty the medical theories of his day under new and not too original trappings. Had Alexander been reborn at the beginning of the nineteenth century, he would in all probability have died of the same disease that had killed him two thousand years before, in spite of the fact that at that time his life could easily have been spared. That such would have been the case was shown by the fate of another man, resembling in many respects the King of Macedonia, a man who died in Greece in 1824, George Gordon, sixth Lord Byron.

Like Alexander, Lord Byron was of extreme beauty, and he too would have dressed like a pagan god had not the gravity of his British surroundings forced him to the compromise of dressing like a dandy. Like Alexander, the English poet felt the attraction of Greece, although the Greece of Lord Byron was but a ragged shadow of Alexander's. For centuries foreign invasions, civil wars, tyrants, partitions, and sporadic anarchy had torn to shreds that unfortunate country where our culture had seen the light of day and which Lord Byron wanted to rescue from the domination of the Turks, who had kept it in abject slavery for more than three and a half centuries. Sad forebodings seemed to have descended upon the English bard when he went to the swampy town of Missolonghi in Greece to wage war against the infidel. Yet with his fears were intermingled strange desires in a dream vaguely like Alexander's. He wanted to exchange the wreath of the poet for that of the hero; to become the great architect and rebuild the glories of Greece; to bring back to life that republic of letters which had had no equal since the days of Pericles.

Lord Byron's dream, however, like that of Alexander, was shattered by the real enemy of Greece. He too fell prey to malaria, was thrown into a state of great agitation, became delirious, and was unable to sleep. Afterward he became greatly depressed, lost his voice, and remained in a comatose condition. Like Alexander, Lord Byron died on the eleventh day of his disease. The physicians, after two thousand years, did no better than those of Alexander: they bled him and gave him some innocuous concoctions; calling it a "fever," they did not know what disease was killing him, much less any remedy that might cure him. Lord Byron was thirty-six years old when he died, Alexander thirty-two, and no other men, dying so young, have left so deep an imprint as these two left on their respective cultures.

A shabby, undernourished mob of guerrilla fighters against the Turks stood with heavy hearts in the square of Missolonghi when the "English nobleman" died. They were certainly a miserable sight compared to their ancestors, the invincible Greek captains of the Macedonian phalanx who, in plumed helmets, shining armor, and crimson capes, also stood with heavy hearts outside Alexander's golden tent when he died; but they were equally brave. The courage of the Greeks had not changed; but neither had there been any change in the disease that had turned their country into a God-forsaken nation, a public battleground where their determination to be a free and respected people was a useless, if not suicidal, attempt, although the mere fact that there was still a Greece ought to command the profoundest admiration.

The plight of the Greeks was the more to be lamented since for two centuries a cure for the disease that ravaged their country had been known. But judging by Lord Byron's unnecessary death, quinine was still an unknown remedy in one of the great malarial regions of the world. At this late day and age public health was still the least worry of statesmen who must have believed illness to be an act of Providence as Alexander himself had believed it to be. Four years after the death of Lord Byron, in 1828, the European powers resolved to interfere in favor of Greece and the French Army occupied the Peloponnesus. In the eight months that the campaign lasted soldiers suffering from malaria had spent seventy-seven thousand days in the hospital; the number of days spent by the wounded was six thousand. Among the officers the rate of malaria had been very low because the French high command was well supplied with quinine.

Greece, however, was but a tiny spot in the enormous area plagued by malaria which comprised three fifths of the whole world. On the island of Corsica eighty per cent of the male population was unfit for military service on account of malaria. In India and in China half the British garrison was admitted to hospitals each year for malaria, and the same was true for the white population in Africa, while in British Guiana as high as eighty per cent of the garrison was attacked yearly by the disease. As for the native population of these countries, the number of malarial patients reached astronomical proportions—hundreds of millions.

And so water, which had been hailed by all ancient civilizations as the bearer of life, was also dreaded as the bearer of death. In Africa it was believed the Jigue, a ghostly black dwarf with long hair, who dwelt in the rivers, took away the life of little children in their sleep. In India Varuna, god of the waters, baldheaded, white, yellow-eyed, and leprous, was the punisher of sinners; and a legend tells of the fair Indian maiden who, being asked in marriage by the king, accepted only on condition that she should never see water. In Scandinavia fevers were contracted by meeting wicked little elves who lived about springs and fountains; monsters of the waters were feared in Denmark, Sweden, Germany, and England. And it took Hercules to confront the revolting Hydra, the nine-headed dweller of swamps and springs, which laid waste the lands about them, but for each head Hercules cut off her, two new ones immediately appeared.

Meanwhile large numbers of quinine-yielding trees grew in South America; but they grew throughout twenty thousand miles of impenetrable forests, and the actual amount of bark available in the market was insignificant compared to the need for it. In French Guiana alone as much as four pounds of quinine for each person was needed in a single year.

The confusion within the ranks of the medical profession added considerably to the scarcity of the drug and did nothing to alleviate the plight of the malarial population. Medicine in fact was in a sore spot. The ancients' explanations as to the causes of disease had been shattered; but the new ones that had been built on their ruins were of necessity insecure. Although "bad air" was still favored by the majority as the immediate cause of malaria, the resulting fit of fever, as in any other feverish disease, was still explained by elegant variations on Hippocrates' theme that fever was an effort of nature to deliver the body from "corrupt matter." To the brain were ascribed mysterious sources of healing energy, called the *primum mobile*, which, when in decline, were restored by a physical commotion resulting in fever; and the existence of a "vital flame" was proposed which was kept burning by uncanny blasts, resulting from external stimuli, and thus the fever was caused by too much blasting activity. A curious medieval flavor can be detected in these theories, appearing in the nineteenth century when the "age of reason" was attaining full maturity. The very phrasing of them was reminiscent of the cloister, where the monastic authorities of the past had speculated on "vital spirits" and "divine powers of healing." Even the old devil was brought back to the medical stage in the United States by a Dr. McElroy who confessed to believing that the fever process was the work of the Great Enemy. To counteract this late folly, however, the soberer physicians flatly stated that all fevers were caused by inflammation of the brain, just as once upon a time all fevers were supposed to be caused by the bile.

Fevers, then, were still considered as the manifestation of one indivisible disease, and the attempt to "map fevers into orders, genera, species and varieties" was denounced by the medical authority, Benjamin Rush, as an attempt to "map and describe the ever-changing clouds in the firmament on a windy day." On this basis extraordinary medical papers appeared, according to which quinine could cure typhoid fever, yellow fever, measles, and the gout; in fact as many diseases as one hundred and fifty years before Dr. Gideon Harvey had said were caused by the very administration of this unfortunate remedy. Public opinion, following the new trend, ran amuck on the subject of quinine, and the people thronged the apothecary shops to buy the drug for the common cold, the toothache, and sore feet. Thus considerable amounts of quinine were miserably wasted.

The extraordinary success attained by an ague curer named Sir Robert Talbor, and the scholarly explanation of this success given by the Italian, Francesco Torti, who proved conclusively how quinine could cure only malaria, had sunk into complete oblivion. A common and lamentable occurrence in the history of science is that of having to rediscover earlier findings subsequently forgotten. Thus it happened that Sir Robert's saga was re-enacted in the nineteenth century, in the United States, where at this late date a great deal of apprehension still prevailed against the Peruvian bark, particularly when administered in large doses, although malaria was a regular plague in the Southern and Western states, spreading throughout New England and as far north as the St. Lawrence River.

Several physicians tried to overcome this apprehension in the young republic, where bleeding and purging and the unlimited use of coffee and whisky were the treatments for malaria, favored particularly by the frontiersmen. But the learned writings of the physicians in favor of the drug did not seem to be as successful as the less scientific procedure used by Dr. John Sappington in the great malarial region of the Mississippi Valley; for, such is the lack of imagination attending prejudice, whether in the cotton belt or in the sophisticated court of Charles II, that in order to make quinine widely used Dr. Sappington had to avail himself of the same means employed by Sir Robert Talbor. Like Sir Robert, Sappington learned about the effectiveness of quinine by experimenting in a malarial region, became opposed to bleeding and purging, and emerged also with a "secret" known as "Sappington's Anti-Fever Pills." Since he had no kings to patronize him, in order to make his secret famous he took recourse to the good old American way of salesmanship through advertisement. He therefore engaged the services of some twenty-five salesmen who, while selling his pills all over the South and West, were the living example of their virtues, since none of them had ever been taken ill though in constant transit through the worst malarial pest-holes. Like Sir Robert, Sappington became a wealthy man with his pills but, unlike the chevalier, he did not sell his secret for a purse of gold, for in the course of time another drug appeared to compete most successfully with his anti-fever patent remedy, another drug known by several names including that of quinine. Whether for this reason or moved by one of nature's noble impulses, Sappington confessed, in a book on "fevers" published in 1844, that quinine indeed was the main component of his pills.

Sappington is a debated figure: some describe him as a great humanitarian, others as a ruthless speculator; some credit him with great medical wisdom, others scarcely rate him as a mediocre practitioner, more in the category of an empiric. Yet one of his most severe critics agrees that, in the United States, he was one of the few to recognize malaria in small children, one of the few to oppose bleeding and purging, and one of the earliest advocates of the use of quinine as a preventive remedy, three achievements which should deserve a fair amount of recognition when viewed against the background of medical knowledge of his day.

It was neither the physician nor the botanist, however, but the chemist who made the next decisive step, after the discovery of the bark, toward the solution of the problem of malaria. In 1816 a Portuguese naval surgeon named Gomez isolated from the Peruvian bark a febrifuge principle which he called cinchonine. Four years later the French chemists, Pelletier and Caventou, discovered that the anti-malarial agent in the bark resided in two alkaloids, one cinchonine, as described by Gomez, and the other, named quinine by the French scientists, which appeared to be more powerful in its action than cinchonine. Pelletier and Caventou, refusing to take a patent, published their method for isolating the alkaloids for everybody's use and the practical consequences of this discovery proved to be of the greatest importance. This method made it possible to determine in a test tube the content of quinine in the different barks from the various species of cinchonas before giving the drug to the patient, who so far had been the test tube himself. And it allowed the preparation of a purified product in the form of sulphate of quinine, a much more powerful drug and much easier to digest than the whole bark, which was very apt to cause vomiting.

The manufacture of sulphate of quinine immediately caught the eye of the chemical companies; it was one of the neatest business propositions in history—on the one hand an inexhaustible supply of bark from the stores of nature and on the other the hugest possible market made up of millions of malarial patients. This commercial utopia, however, was marred from the beginning by a number of obstacles. With the new chemical procedure it was found that the bark with the highest content of quinine came neither from Peru nor from Colombia, once known as the New Kingdom of Granada, but from Bolivia, where grew the particular species named *Cinchona calisaya*, the latest to come into the market and in negligible amounts.

If very little was known of the cinchonas from Peru and Colombia, nothing was known of the *Cinchona calisaya* from Bolivia, although it had been studied by the unfortunate Joseph de Jussieu, who seems not to have missed a single cinchona tree in all of South America in the most amazing feat of scientific exploration known; but his manuscripts were irretrievably lost. Now if sulphate of quinine was to be manufactured in any considerable amount, more *Cinchona calisaya* was needed, which meant regulation of the gathering of the bark at the source and provision for the conservation of this invaluable species. But how could this be accomplished? As in the days when the Jesuits exported the bark, in Bolivia too only the forest Indians knew how to find the calisaya, by means comparable to those used by a hound following a scent. On a ridge overlooking the foliage of the trees a forest Indian could detect at a tremendous distance a group of cinchonas, ascertaining moreover to what species they belonged by the ruffling of their leaves in the breeze and by differences in their shades of color, all absolutely indistinguishable to anyone else. If unable to survey from an altitude, he would detect the tree within the forest by the appearance of the trunk and even by watching the dry leaves on the ground, knowing whence the cinchona leaves had come, had they been carried by the wind.

The forest Indians in Bolivia, as in Peru and Colombia, thus formed the bulk of the *cascarilleros* or bark collectors, for only a forest Indian and one of the purest breed could enter the forest at random and subsequently find his way out. As a rule they went in search of the tree in family parties, father, mother, and children, and came back a week later with a certain amount of bark, some good, some useless, all stripped by the quickest procedure, which resulted usually in the death of the trees. It was obvious, however, that any attempt to place each one of these bark-collecting parties under some form of supervision was a physical impossibility. The cultivation of the cinchona tree in limited areas seemed to be the only solution to the problem and a strong demand for it sprang from certain quarters as a result of the sudden concern for the fate of millions of malarial patients all over the world.

It was up to the South American countries to lend a careful ear to those portents. But the South American countries, recently emancipated from Spain, were passing through the pains of childhood and, too busy with their own civil wars and their fights with each other over boundaries and the like, could not concentrate on botanical experiments. As a result of the ever increasing demand for *Cinchona calisaya* the forests of Bolivia were overrun by hordes of cascarilleros, who in no time left the most accessible regions bare of these precious trees. So great was the fear that this species might become extinct that the Bolivian Government, suddenly aware of its priceless possession, made fruitless attempts to limit the exports of calisaya bark; but it would have required the largest police force in the world to stop the Indian cascarilleros from going into the forest in search of the tree. The Bolivian Government, moreover, was hampered by the political situation, which was in hopeless confusion all over South America.

Thus the advisability of entrusting the custody of the priceless cinchonas to more reasonable nations—France, England, Belgium, or Holland—which had at their command colonies with suitable climates and large supplies of cheap labor, began to take shape as an enterprise "deserving the blessing of all civilized mankind." But good as these intentions were, they could not be carried out because toward the middle of the nineteenth century, as far as concerned its botanical features, the world still knew nothing of the fever bark tree.

And then another page was turned back in the family album of history and from a blurred engraving certain legendary characters came uncannily to life. In 1843 the French

Government again sent to South America a scientific expedition whose chief was the Count of Castelnau, an indefatigable traveler, elegant with his pen and a sophisticated man of the world, so reminiscent of Charles Marie de la Condamine that it makes one ponder over the mysteries of reincarnation. To this expedition were attached two naturalists, a Viscount d'Osery and Dr. H. A. Weddell, whose purpose was to study the fever bark tree. The curiosity of Castelnau and his colleagues about the natural secrets of the New World had been aroused by a professor of botany named Adrien de Jussieu, the fifth of his family to become eminent in this field, and the great-nephew of Joseph de Jussieu of sorrowful memory. And so these men were lured into undertaking this voyage by the beckoning finger of a tragic ghost who roamed the South American forests after his other mutilated self had died insane in urban Paris. They had seen Jussieu's description of the fever bark tree and were determined to finish the task, in spite of the warning given them by the weird remarks interspersed with the text of that strange document. But the members of Castelnau's expedition were coolheaded men of the nineteenth century who did not believe in ghosts or in protective divinities of the forest; and they were wrong.

Although no quarrels or rivalries have been reported among them, misfortune pursued the group as it had pursued La Condamine's expedition. They landed in Brazil and, after exploring across this country for two years, reached Bolivia, whence they started toward Peru by the Urubamba River. They were traveling through a region inhabited by wild forest Indians when, on waking up one morning, they found that their guides had escaped, leaving them headed toward a dangerous waterfall. Death seemed inevitable and Castelnau,

determined to save the numerous manuscripts already gathered, ordered the youngest member of the group, the twenty-
eight-year-old D'Osery, to risk finding his way to Lima with
the baggage. D'Osery reached Lima and immediately thereafter started toward the Amazon region where his companions
had miraculously escaped. The local authorities supplied him
with four guides who knew their way perfectly through the
jungle; and this they certainly did because they were Jivaros,
wild Indians of the forest noted for their ferocity, who had
made a dubious compromise with the ways of the white man.
D'Osery with his baggage started with the guides up the
Marañon River and was never seen again. It was said that his
guides had murdered him.

A party was sent up the Marañon to look for his body.
The Jivaros, at the beating of drums, came to the banks of
the river, in full war attire, with lances and arrows. On learning of the white man's errand, however, they became friendly;
yes, they had seen the foreigner. He had stayed with them
but they had not harmed him because they liked him, for he
was the Apo, meaning in their tongue the man of wisdom,
deserving of veneration. At the thought of D'Osery's death
the Jivaros in fact felt such grief that, falling on their knees,
they asked to be baptized. Perhaps D'Osery had not been
killed after all but had been captured by the Jivaros because
he was the Apo; and perhaps he reached a happy and honorable old age, as the all-wise, surrounded by his devoted wives
and a respectable number of children. Unless the great wisdom perceived in him by the Jivaros became too much of a
temptation to this people who later on became famous by
mastering the curious art of preserving human heads shrunk
to a third of their size and could not possibly have resisted

the opportunity of preserving so extraordinary a specimen.

Whatever his fate, the forces that had brought about D'Osery's disappearance had lost their usual keenness of perception, since they had destroyed the wrong man and the wrong documents. He who was really looking for the fever bark tree was not D'Osery but Weddell.

Leaving Castelnau, Weddell explored the Andes for two years, scouting for the cinchonas, with no more than the usual mishaps of being regularly left by his guides and having a couple of mules roll down the precipitous slopes of those impressive mountains. In 1847 he reached Cuzco, in Peru, whence he intended to explore the forests of Bolivia in search of the famous *Cinchona calisaya;* and in Cuzco he had a pathetic encounter. There he found a compatriot named Delondre, in a very despondent condition, full of ailments, feverish, covered with rashes, and greatly dejected physically as well as morally. After many civilities between the two Frenchmen, Weddell naturally wondered what M. Delondre could be doing in Cuzco. M. Delondre was rather vague at first but after some diplomatic repartee he admitted that he too was looking for the *Cinchona calisaya.* He was no botanist, nor yet a scientist in any branch; neither was he an explorer, or otherwise interested in nature; he was something much simpler and far nearer ordinary mortals: the first manufacturer of sulphate of quinine on an international scale. Still, he was a crusader in his own right, for industry was the great adventure of the nineteenth century and this forerunner of the modern magnates who make fabulous transactions by telephone in sumptuous offices full of secretaries still had in his veins the blood of those adventurous merchants who brought silk and spices from the Orient, ivory from Africa, silver and medicinal herbs from the Spanish Indies, and priceless furs from the Hudson Bay.

And so M. Delondre, true to his blood, being unable to obtain enough calisaya bark in Europe, had come to get it from its natural habitat, with the purpose moreover of processing it *sur place*. Thus he had brought along some extraordinary machinery which had been assembled with astonishing success in Valparaiso, in a factory for the manufacture of sulphate of quinine. One thing, however, had gone wrong: there was no bark to be had. The Bolivian Government, in an effort to regulate the exploitation of the cinchonas, had sold the bark-collecting concession to Messrs. Pinto and Company on the stipulation that only a limited amount of bark would be stripped each year. And Messrs. Pinto and Company, not interested in M. Delondre's venture, had sold their entire output of bark to a powerful New York company. M. Delondre denounced these dealings as a monopoly, asserted his right to manufacture quinine in the name of Pelletier's and Caventou's discovery, and, disregarding Messrs. Pinto and Company's agreement with the government, made arrangements with two individuals who promised to supply him with the necessary calisaya bark. But of his two new associates, one was murdered by the forest Indians and the other committed suicide; and so the bark never arrived. At this point M. Delondre, having spent a considerable amount of time and money, found himself saddled with a factory and no bark, and collapsed; he became very ill and had given himself up to complete despair when Weddell chanced to discover him.

Somehow the presence of his countryman gave him new strength, and he recovered from his spiritual and bodily ills to the point of accompanying Weddell in his search for the *Cinchona calisaya*. They went to the forests which lay between southern Peru and northern Bolivia and where the calisaya was supposed to grow in a comparatively small area. Although they found excellent guides, who opened a path for them through the jungle up the mountain, it was a dreadful journey, always climbing under sheets of rain. They had reached the point of complete exhaustion when they heard from the top of the mountain, where one of the Indians had preceded them, the blows of an ax against a tree. It was the *Cinchona calisaya* which the Indian was felling so that they might see it in the thickness of the forest.

Later M. Delondre, describing the great moment, wrote: "We were exhausted but the blows of the ax, which were the signal of our conquest, revived our strength as by enchantment and very soon we were near that great and magnificent tree which I was seeing for the first time, and which for so long had been the object of my dreams. I remained in ecstasies, gazing at its beautiful silvery bark, at its large leaves of a green-brownish color, and at its flowers with the sweetish perfume, slightly reminiscent of the lilac." What the scientist and the explorer had failed to do the industrialist did; he uttered the first words of admiration for that tree, evaluated thus far only in terms of its utilitarian function; he presented it with the first tribute to its great and much neglected beauty.

The tribute must have broken the spell, for the gods of the forest granted to the industrialist what they had denied to the scientist and even to the philanthropist, resenting perhaps the interference in their designs of these would-be saviors of mankind, whereas the lyric M. Delondre, conscious of his human limitations, wanted only to turn into solid gold the "silvery bark" of that noble plant. A new element had now entered the history of quinine, to which great forces, whether natural or mythological, were going to surrender within the next decades in the gigantic sway of the Industrial Revolution, in which malaria was to play an all-important role, for industry was going to grow outside the range of malarial countries.

Both Delondre and Weddell returned safely to Cuzco, where they were graciously entertained by the native aristocracy and proceeded to Arequipa, escorted by a group of gallant caballeros. Weddell took ship for France and Delondre went back to his factory, which failed a year later, a victim of the early clashes for monopolies in the arena.

On his return to France Weddell published in 1849 *Histoire naturelle des quinquinas,* the first comprehensive study of this tree, of which he described not less than nineteen species, together with much information as to its geographical distribution and a reasonably complete study of the *Cinchona calisaya.* This work was preceded by a learned foreword by Adrien de Jussieu. The world at last knew something of the fever bark tree. What is more, the world saw the fever bark tree. Weddell had taken to France seeds of the *Cinchona calisaya,* of which some were given to the English Government, and thus in the hothouses of Paris and London the first cinchonas outside the American hemisphere were born. Of these, a young plant was given to the Dutch Government, on whose orders it was sent to Java, where it took happy root, grew, bloomed, and produced a number of healthy descendants. Whatever forces the wild Indians of the forest had invoked to protect their tree had most certainly lost their power, and the wild Indians of the forest lost their tree.

CHAPTER IX

Scientific Interlude

Hippocrates took medicine from the hands of the priest and gave it to the natural philosopher; this was no mean accomplishment, for the priest had been the absolute healer since the first medicine man undertook to frighten away the demons of disease. Moreover the philosopher, disregarding popular belief, claimed that diseases were caused not by demons or the like but by changes within the body brought about by agencies of an earthly nature. What these agencies were the philosopher did not know, but he decided to find out by the self-rewarding process of pondering over them in violent exercises of mental speculation.

Ingenious theories of great elegance were the result of these mental exercises; but when the scientist came along and made an attempt to put these theories to the test of experiment the philosopher grew angry and did to the scientist what the medicine man had done to him: he treated the scientist as a heretic, banned him from the community, and kept him paralyzed for centuries.

The scientist nevertheless made brave attacks now and again against the fortress of pure thought represented by the medical philosopher. But these attacks, however damaging, had accomplished nothing so far as the practical application of medicine was concerned, for in no way had they contributed a logical explanation of the causes of disease. The most or-

iginal attempt in this direction was the Italian Fracastoro's
assertion in the fifteenth century that diseases were caused
not by changes in the humors, but by external agents or
germs, "endowed with the faculty of multiplying themselves
very rapidly."

The philosopher thus was still supreme until the middle of
the nineteenth century, when a French chemist named Louis
Pasteur engaged in certain unspectacular experiments in
search of the mechanism responsible for the fermentation of
wine, a great trial to the wine industry since time immemorial. The results of Pasteur's experiments, however, were far
from unspectacular, for he maintained that living organisms,
infinitesimal in size, by multiplying and propagating themselves very rapidly in the wine, were the cause of its fermentation. There fell immediately upon the bewildered chemist a
storm of protests launched by the great authority in chemistry, the German Liebig, who had worked for years on the
problem of fermentation, which he ascribed to chemical
changes without the intervention of any living matter whatsoever.

Liebig and his followers did not know what they were going to learn very soon: namely, that Pasteur was a virtuoso
of the test tube and could prove his conclusions with experiments as ingenious as they were easy to grasp. Thus he showed
beyond doubt that the fermentation of wine was caused by
minute living organisms which he described as having the
shape of small globules. And what was the origin of these
globules? Did they appear in the wine by spontaneous generation? No, was Pasteur's answer, they came from without,
and each globule had descended from another globule since

the first of them appeared on earth, their origin being that of life itself.

Now fermentation, that turned wine from a clear, savory liquid into a turbid, ill-tasting brew, had been regarded as a disease of the wine. According to Pasteur, therefore, these living globules, visible only through the microscope, by getting into the wine made the wine "sick." The great truth, with the simplicity always inherent to it, became manifest: living organisms, infinitesimal in size, by invading the wine made it sick and by invading the human flesh made man sick.

Pasteur began his researches on fermentation about 1857. Ten years later the English surgeon Lister wrote the following: "When it had been shown by the researches of Pasteur that the septic properties of the atmosphere depended . . . on minute organisms suspended in it . . . it occurred to me that decomposition in the injured part might be avoided . . . by applying as a dressing some material capable of destroying the life of the floating particles. . . ." Sterile surgery had begun, and with it ended the horror of infected wounds, of "hospital stench" which penetrated blocks away, of that nightmare of suppuration considered as a salutary deliverance of corrupt humors, those accursed humors that had caused more human suffering than all the wars mankind has fought.

In 1876 the German practitioner, Robert Koch, published his memorable paper on anthrax, showing that this ailment was produced by living organisms shaped like rods, found in the blood of animals suffering from the disease. They had been observed twenty-six years before by the French veterinarian, Davaine, who had called them "bacteria." By 1881, Pasteur had found a vaccine against anthrax. Thus the new science of bacteriology was born and its first steps formed the most dramatic sequence of events in the history of science. In 1882, Koch found the bacteria that cause tuberculosis and two years later those responsible for Asiatic cholera.

That fever was not a disease but a symptom common to nearly all diseases, regardless of their cause, became now an established fact. Thus the attempt to discover the cause of diseases by studying the nature of fevers had been as vain as if by observing the shadows made by sunlight one had tried to discover the cause of solar energy. As the shadows give the position of the sun, so is fever a sure sign of disease —the result of it but not its cause.

And what was the cause of malarial fevers? The first known definite answer to this question had been given by a man of great knowledge who lived in the first century B.C., of whom very little is known because most of his works are unfortunately lost. He was a Roman patrician named Marcus Terentius Varro, a poet and scholar, described as the most learned of the Romans, who was made by Caesar director of the public library of Rome. Varro seems to have been a universal genius who wrote brilliantly on every possible subject including husbandry, which he discusses at length in his *Rerum Rusticarum*, miraculously preserved. He contends that in the marshes there grow animals too small to be seen, which enter the human body and cause disease. Now and again reference was made through the centuries to Varro's suggestion, particularly in the eighteenth century, by another famous Italian named Lancisi, who strongly advocated the drainage of the swamps as a precaution against malaria and who made some curious studies on the mosquito concerning the spread of the disease, although mosquitoes are far from invisible.

After Pasteur's discoveries it was a foregone conclusion that Varro's invisible "animalcule" was one of the newly found bacteria, but this proved to be the wrong conclusion. The greatest medical discovery of all times failed to throw any light on one of the oldest and greatest of medical problems; malaria appeared to belong to a group of diseases in which none of the new germs could be found and which, moreover, escaped the rules laid down by the new science of bacteriology, in that these diseases were not contagious, although occurring simultaneously in a number of individuals in a given locality. It seemed as if the animals too small to be seen growing in the marshes were a mythical fabrication of Caesar's highly imaginative librarian.

In spite of these failures the search was continued for the animalcule, bacteria, or whatever it was that caused malaria, and among those looking for it was a French Army medical officer named Charles Louis Alphonse Laveran. Born in Paris in 1845, he was the son and grandson of physicians through his father, also an army medical officer of distinction, and descended through his mother from a long line of famous army men of nobility. With this background it is no wonder that Laveran should have been endowed with a partiality for order, method, and discipline, three characteristics which, knit together by an unusual intelligence and a persistent power of observation, he earnestly applied to the solution of the problem of malaria. But before he could devote himself to these studies he had to go through the Franco-Prussian War to see his country in 1870 surrendered to the Prussians. He was in charge of a military hospital in Metz which was besieged by the Germans. Young Laveran knew in full the horrors of war, with thousands of wounded and epidemics spreading in the city, without medical supplies, linen, or food, a tragic event which he never forgot and which turned him into the tireless champion of military hygiene as a factor as important to the strength of an army as weapons and ammunitions. In 1878, Laveran attained the rank of major and was sent to Algeria, first to Bône, then to Biskra, and finally to the military hospital of Constantine.

Never had the French Army made so wise an appointment, for Major Laveran, immediately on his arrival, undertook the study of malaria for the very good reason, as he naïvely explained, that, "being stationed in Algeria, I felt that I should naturally take advantage of the situation to study those fevers which, by their frequence and noxiousness, should be foremost in engaging the attention of any physician coming to this province." That he was to tackle the most puzzling of medical riddles seemed to be of no consequence to the major, who, bound by a sense of discipline, had obviously decided that when a man is faced with a problem so overwhelming in terms of human lives and suffering, the only thing for him to do is to attempt its solution.

Being also a man of method, Laveran first chose the field in which he was to fight his battle. Varro had said nineteen centuries before that a living thing causing disease grew in the marshes, and much later Lancisi had added that from the marshes it passed into the air. But no living thing causing malaria had been found in the water, the air, or the soil in spite of a diligent search centuries old. Laveran did not know whether the cause of malaria might reside in any of these places; but there was one place in which he was certain of its presence and that was obviously in the malarial patients themselves. In Constantine he had hordes of such patients and he began obeying a probably atavistic impulse, the study of their humors—that is, of their blood, which he felt had been greatly neglected and where he suspected the cause of their ailment might lie.

There was not much to differentiate the blood of malarial patients from that of other individuals; when seen through a microscope, red cells and white cells floated as usual in yellowish fluid. Yet in the blood of malarial patients there was something—a peculiar pigment—tiny round black spots which could be seen within the white cells. It was a well-known phenomenon, and, the white cells being called leucocytes, these spotted ones were called melaniferous leucocytes, melanin being the name given to the pigment. All malarial patients seemed to have these pigmented cells and a number of investigators had observed the fact without going any further. Laveran, however, was a stubborn soldier and a lover of logic. If malarial patients had pigmented cells, the pigment had to come from somewhere before entering the white cells. He thus persisted in looking through his microscope at countless smears of blood hour after hour, day after day, month after month. He saw nothing but the confounded polka-dotted cells, yet he kept on looking.

Laveran had to look until he was blind from searching, for he was chained to his microscope by that power, so seldom manifest, and loosely defined as the desire for knowledge, the quest for the unknown, or simply curiosity. Now and again a man falls victim to this power and, oblivious of whether his children have any bread, of his country's struggles, and of whether he himself has a roof over his head, he looks at something as Copernicus looked at the stars, Galileo looked at a pendulum, Newton looked at an apple, and Columbus looked at a seemingly endless ocean. It is a cruel power, for many a man has looked at something to the end of his life only to see nothing because he lacked either the ability or the means to evaluate his observations, and so died scorned as a worthless member of his community or at best pitied as the victim of some strange form of lunacy. A few have been lucky: Laveran belonged to this chosen minority.

He continued to look at his cells and at long last he saw something because his gaze had shifted from the white cells to the red ones near by; he saw within them a peculiar object. It was a kind of bluish-white sphere, like a soap bubble, with a tiny red dot at one point on its surface and black pin points scattered about it. This curious sphere moved, like an amoeba in undulant motion. Was this thing alive within the cell? Eventually the sphere began to enlarge and so did the red dot, till it broke in two and then in four and then in eight . . . while the bluish-white sphere kept enlarging until it filled the red cell, which then burst, and the red dots floated free in the yellowish fluid of the blood, where they took bizarre shapes. They enlarged and curved themselves like a Turkish crescent with the red dot in the center; some took the shape of an egg, whereas in others long filaments stuck out like the tentacles of an octopus. While all these extraordinary things took place, fragments of the torn red cells and a number of the black pin points swam loose; the white cells, whose task it is to destroy any dead matter in the blood stream, swallowed it all and became the pigmented cells, the melaniferous leucocytes typical of malarial patients. But Laveran knew now whence came the pigment. It was the detritus, the gory remains resulting from that incredible multiplication of red dots, reproducing themselves at the expense of the red cells of man, as indispensable to him as the air he breathes or the water he drinks. A murderous process of destruction no less terrifying for taking place in the world of the infinitely small, since it had done away with more lives than any catastrophe occurring in the world of the infinitely large.

To see all this for the first time through the microscope, when the composition of normal blood itself was hardly known, was a tour de force requiring a sixth sense of perception which Laveran obviously possessed. In two preliminary notes which he sent to the Academy of Medicine of Paris he wrote down with great care and detail all this story of spheres and red dots propagating themselves in the blood, concluding that these spheres and red dots were nothing but parasites, the cause of malarial fevers. Laveran was a lucky man, for the credulity of the scientific world had reached unexpected leniency following the staggering discoveries of Pasteur. Thus when it fell to Léon Colin, one of the great advocates of "bad air" as the cause of the malarial fevers, to read Laveran's notes to the solemn and bearded Academy of Medicine, Colin was full of tolerance and even understanding for the phantasy of a colonial physician, suffering probably from the effects of the African sun. For how could anyone contend that malaria was caused by a living parasite when it had been established since time immemorial that malaria was not transmitted from person to person? How then could that peculiar parasite spread the disease if it did not go from person to person like the bacteria recently discovered by Pasteur and Koch?

In 1880 Alphonse Laveran presented to the Academy of Medicine of Paris the complete paper of his discoveries, ending with one of the shortest conclusions ever appended to any paper, in which, without argument or apologies, he stated in an uncompromising fashion what to him was the explanation of his findings: "The accidents of malarial fevers are caused by the introduction in the blood of parasitic elements which take the different shapes above described; it is because it kills these parasites that sulphate of quinine puts a stop to the accidents of malarial fevers." Whoever cared to read this could accept it or reject it. Laveran was not to discuss it.

According to Laveran, then, quinine cured malaria because it attacked the parasite that caused the disease. With one exception, therefore, quinine was a drug unique among the infinite number of remedies used in medicine. Purgatives, sedatives, or stimulants, which alleviate pain, bring about repose, help the heart, or arrest symptoms such as bleeding, coughing, or choking, are most helpful when properly used in aiding the patient through his ailments. But these are not curative drugs, properly speaking, like quinine, which makes the sick well by striking at the very core of the disease. Quinine's only equal in this army of lesser drugs was mercury for the treatment of syphilis. This also destroys the agent causing the disease but its toxicity, absent in quinine, eventually led to its dethronement by other compounds, leaving quinine the undisputed sovereign of all natural remedies and yet the most violently opposed of all known remedies. Only in our time and by the ingenuity of man has quinine been robbed of its solitary splendor: in 1935 Gerhard Domagk in Germany published his memorable paper on the therapeutic virtues of the sulpha drugs, and in 1941 Sir Howard Florey and his co-workers wrote their no less memorable paper on the curative powers of penicillin, discovered in 1929 by Sir Alexander Fleming.

Laveran's discovery was greeted first with reserve. The

medical world had grown weary of so many discoveries in so short a time; they were still wondering about the veracity of Pasteur's observations when another blow was dealt to their peace of mind, since it was obvious that Laveran's parasite was not bacteria but a far more complex organism scientifically known as protozoan. If Laveran was right, then these protozoa he had found in the blood of French soldiers in Algeria would have to be found in the blood of millions of people everywhere. By 1890, ten years after the discovery, in Russia, in the United States, in India, all over the world, papers had appeared in all languages stating that Laveran's parasite had been found in malarial patients of all races and of all ages.

Honors rained upon the army physician, the "founder of tropical medicine," as he was called when awarded the Nobel prize in 1907, and the great defender of military hygiene. Alphonse Laveran died in Paris on May 18, 1920, at the age of seventy-seven. He worked to the end in the Institute for Tropical Diseases he himself had endowed with his Nobel prize money. Free from the dull ambitions and petty miseries that fill the hearts of lesser men, he had devoted himself for fifty years to the welfare of mankind, to which he had rendered great service.

The first scientists to realize in full the importance of Laveran's discovery were a group of Italian investigators— Marchiafava, Celli, Grassi, Golgi—who in 1885 began a systematic study of the blood of malarial patients in order to put together with unique perseverance and skill the pieces of that Chinese puzzle Laveran had laid on the table, the natural history of the malarial parasite. One by one the pieces fell into place: the sphere with the red dot which divided itself within the red cell, first in two, then in four, and so on, until the red cell broke up, continued to repeat this process of destruction over and over again, each new sphere entering a new cell, dividing itself within it, and destroying it unless medication with quinine was instituted, which immediately reduced the number of parasites. It was when the red cells broke up and the parasites became free in the blood stream that the paroxysm of fever occurred; and since the time taken by the spheres to reproduce themselves within the cell varies, in some cases every forty-two hours, in others seventy hours, the result is the tertian or quartan fevers. These differences in the behavior of the parasite are due to the fact that there are three kinds of parasite, which at first seemed identical, and which eventually were named malaria, vivax, and falciparum. All of these as well as far more subtle and elusive phases in the life cycle of the parasite were described by the Italian scientists, who were rendering a great service to science and to their country, for at the end of the nineteenth century malaria was a staggering problem in Italy.

In 1870 Italy had become a united kingdom and the first provisions of the new regime were directed toward ridding Rome of its ancient curse. Great works of urbanization, drainage, and sewage were started, which immediately produced gratifying results. But in the Campagna around the city the problem seemed hopeless. Attempts were made to drain the swamps, agricultural colonies were started, and in the process hundreds of healthy laborers and farmers from other locations died. The hospitals of Rome became crowded with these unfortunate people who dragged themselves to the city, thereby bringing new sources of infection. Sanitary stations were instituted in the Campagna and quinine was distributed; but of the first eleven doctors who started these services three died and only one was able to remain for the ten years required to retire with a pension. The infectiousness of the Roman Campagna was such that medication with quinine, even if carried out on a tremendous scale, could serve only to keep the people strong enough to take whatever measures were necessary for the ultimate eradication of the disease.

But to achieve this end there had to be found a very large piece missing from the puzzle the Italian investigators were so skillfully putting together. Where did the parasite found by Laveran come from before attacking man? From the marshes, as the Roman patrician had said? But where in the marshes: in the water, in the air, in the soil? While speculation on the subject ran high, in the United States a physician with boundless imagination, endowed by his British parents with the name of Albert Freeman Africanus King, amused himself with idle speculations as to the mechanism responsible for the spread of malaria, though his official activities concerned the more down-to-earth teaching of obstetrics. Dr. King came forth with a strange paper stating that mosquitoes were the carriers of the disease and giving no less than nineteen reasons in support of this theory—that malaria increased with the mosquito season, that measures against the mosquito protected also against malaria, and so on. Others before King had suggested this possibility of the mosquito, but never before had the case been so thoroughly documented as in King's paper.

Yet it found no recognition whatsoever among his American colleagues. The very expert who had furnished King with the life history of the mosquito had no patience with the malaria theory. The whole proposition was deemed fantastic, not only on its possible merits but because of Dr. King's reputation as a man of too many ideas and too much imagination,

the greatly resented type of person who insists in driving
everybody else to undue exercises of the mind. Notwithstanding this and similar failures, Dr. King stuck to his teaching of
obstetrics for forty-five years in the National Medical College
in Washington, D.C. In 1914, while carrying on one of his
classes, he died at the age of seventy-three, an embittered old
man, and small wonder. When he published his paper on
malaria in 1883, though Laveran had announced his discovery
three years earlier, King knew nothing of it because of the
general indifference that greeted the new parasite. Thus he
had failed to crown his very sound nineteen reasons with the
twentieth and conclusive one, and thus confound his opponents; the chance to make a great discovery by the sheer process
of deduction, like those astronomical discoveries done solely
by calculations on paper, had passed him by. Yet his very
ignorance of Laveran's discovery should make his paper a
greater testimony to the power of his imaginative genius in
putting together as a whole a number of scattered and ostensi-
bly unrelated observations.

Two years after King's paper had appeared Laveran, who
seemed to have heard of his reasonings, made the suggestion
that his parasite might live temporarily in the mosquito—a suggestion which some eleven years later was proved to be true
by the researches of another medical officer, this time of the
British Army, named Ronald Ross. While stationed in India,
Ross showed by means of some involved experiments that
mosquitoes could transmit in birds a disease very similar to
malaria. A mosquito bit a sick bird, sucking the blood with
the parasite, and then bit a healthy bird, into which he injected
the parasite contained in his saliva. Ross was sure that the
same mechanism was responsible for the spread of malaria in

man but he was not able to prove it because he was working with the wrong kind of mosquito. It was the turn of the Italian investigators to complete Ross's investigations as they had completed Laveran's and to show that only the mosquito belonging to the anopheline family was able to pass malaria from the sick to the well.

The great riddle of the connection between malaria and stagnant waters was solved and with its solution curious beliefs as old as mankind became meaningful: the universal fear of the sunset hour, when the young were admonished to get indoors and to stay away from rivers and marshes, the vapors of which might cause shivering, when the windows were shut to keep out the dangerous evening air, when those who had to go out covered themselves even in warm weather, seeking protection from unfelt but dangerous dampness that gave man the chills. What the physicians had missed for thousands of years the people knew: that whatever the agency that gave the fevers, it struck when the first shadows of night came upon the earth.

Varro's animalcule too small to be seen was a reality, though it bred not in the water, the air, or the soil but in the mosquito, as Lancisi in Italy had suspected and as King in America had nearly proved. Among the many varieties of mosquitoes, only the anopheles is capable of performing the amazing feat; the beginnings of malaria are lost in the dim recesses of history, but the anopheles is a sturdy family, and a prolific one that populates the world in numbers comparable to those of the sands of the ocean or the stars in the sky.

Three elements therefore are indispensable for the occurrence of malaria: man, the parasite, and the anopheles, and the disappearance of any one of these three elements will bring about the disappearance of the disease. To destroy the parasite in man would be an almost impossible procedure, since in some forms of malaria, though quinine eliminates the paroxysms, thus making life bearable to the patient, it does not completely eliminate the parasites from the blood. So the patient, although cured to all purposes, is a carrier and a potential source of infection. In other cases, however, although the parasites have completely disappeared from the blood, the patient ten, twenty, or thirty years later may have a relapse unexplainable on the ground of reinfection.

The destruction of the anopheles therefore appears to be the quickest and surest way to eradicate the disease. But this requires public works of drainage and urbanization that only resourceful communities can afford and the people living in malarial areas are far from resourceful because they are sick. To break this vicious circle a systematic distribution of the drug would be required, to give to the malarial populations the necessary physical strength to fight the primary sources of the disease. And to achieve this end, as in a miracle of the gospel, the remedy that can protect man from the ravages of the parasite that has followed him to the four corners of the earth is produced by nature as easily as a weed, in quantities as fabulous as there are victims of the disease.

The physician, fighting a gallant battle against his more conservative colleagues, had introduced quinine into medicine. The missionary, the botanist, and the explorer, fighting sinister odds, had dragged from the fearsome jungles the secret of the fever bark tree. The scientist, with the single weapon of his mind, had laid bare the complex saga of the cause of the disease. Their task was done and the time had now come for the statesman, the economist, the sociologist, the public health worker, with the aid of those who had at their command the great resources of the world, to make use of the acquired knowledge in order to save mankind from the merciless Hydra of the swamps, the monster with nine heads that laid waste the lands. Notwithstanding the legend that two new heads immediately appeared for each one destroyed, the undertaking was far from hopeless, for the monster was not immortal, since the legend had also said that when the right head should be struck the Hydra would die.

CHAPTER X

Poor Man's Quinine

The wild Indians lost their tree, though but for an accident of fate they might have kept it forever. One *Cinchona calisaya*, the variety with the highest quinine content, had survived the rigors of transplantation and had perpetuated itself in Java. The logical conclusion seemed to be that what had been done with one calisaya could be done with any number. But the *Cinchona calisaya* had been found so far only in Bolivia, where the government had reached another conclusion no less logical: that no seeds or young trees were to be taken out of the country no matter for what purpose.

In spite of the political confusion prevailing in the country and the difficulties involved in regulating the exploitation of the cinchonas, there was no fear that the people would betray the government in this resolution, for in the highlands of Bolivia, where the *Cinchona calisaya* grew, there lived a strange and formidable Indian nation; strange and formidable not because of aggressiveness, for they are kind and peaceful, or because of a particularly sophisticated culture, for they are simple and austere, but because of their deep, passionate love for the land that has supported them for countless generations.

Known as the Aymara Indians, they have lived for time out of mind on impressive Lake Titicaca, as large as a small ocean and enclosed within the Andean mountains to form a landscape of unequaled majesty and beauty. This winding lake with its deep inlets separated from one another by high ranges or swift-moving torrents divided the Aymaras into small and completely isolated agricultural communities, from which there was little likelihood of escape except to certain death in the wilderness of the impenetrable mountains. His small plot of ground was therefore to the Aymara food, shelter, and safety. He came to look upon the soil as his only means of survival and in return bestowed upon it an uncommon veneration, combined with the unspoken promise never to part with it and a fiery determination never to let an intruder set foot upon it. When the soil betrayed him and there was no crop and the Aymara was faced with starvation, he sold his child but never his land.

Eventually intruders appeared. First there were the Quechua Indians, who as conquerors made the Aymaras part of the great Inca Empire, probably a matter of indifference to them as the Quechuas did not interfere with their mode of life. The Quechuas themselves became an agricultural nation and the Inca rulers made wise laws of land and labor distribution partly derived from the Aymaras' own legislation. If they asked for part of the crops as tribute it was granted in fairness; and when only the portion allotted to the community was raised the tribute was not collected. The tribute, furthermore, was equally divided in three parts: one to support certain fabulous high priests who worshiped the sun in temples of solid gold, according to the tales, in the faraway city of Cuzco; another to support the great household of the Inca king; but the third was put away in granaries all over the empire and when the crops failed the granaries were opened, food was distributed, and the Aymaras did not go hungry as they had formerly done. The Quechuas were enterprising people; they built towns and roads that connected the isolated communities of the Aymaras, who for the first time went to market through fertile valleys and richer lands but came back to their meager settlements in the mountains without the slightest hesitation or regret.

Then came the Spaniards. The Quechuas were no longer masters of the land and the Aymaras now belonged to a greater empire than the Inca had ever been. Again this was a matter of indifference to them since the Spaniards at first did not interfere with their mode of life, the new invaders being too busy looking for great riches, like the gold they had found in Cuzco. The Aymaras of the highlands, now related to many of the Quechua blood, from their mountaintops watched the conquistadors on beautiful beasts galloping up and down the valleys in a frantic race to conquer the world. But one day the conquistador began to slow down in his pace, for the riches that had lured him were dwindling rapidly, and for the first time he looked at the great land he had conquered—a rich and beautiful land. Then he stopped short in his course, realizing the absurdity of his search for gold; he knew that what he wanted was the land.

Swift calamity now descended upon the Aymara of the highlands, for, on his refusal to give up the land, the Spaniard demolished his hut and his corral and threatened to scorch the land he could not possess. Rather than see his land destroyed, the Aymara gave it to the Spaniard; but the conquistador had to take with the land the Aymara, who remained on the soil of his ancestors as a slave to the usurper, as did his son and his grandson. It was a harsh struggle, none the less tragic for having been comparatively bloodless; the passive courage of the Aymaras was such that, partly through the interference of the Spanish Crown in their behalf, many of the small Indian communities about Lake Titicaca remain intact to this day. As for those who submitted to the conqueror, mitigation came when the Spaniard married the daughter of the Aymara, had children by her, and these children with Spanish names then owned the Indian lands as their rightful heritage. Unruly and determined like his Spanish father, the new American yet felt for the soil where he was born the same devotion his mother's Indian ancestors had felt since time immemorial.

It was these Aymaras, partly Quechuas and now often related to those of Spanish blood (whose love of the land is worthy of a narrative in the best Homeric tradition), whom destiny had appointed as guardians of the *Cinchona calisaya,* the queen and prize of the large family of cinchonas that populates the South American forests. Better guardians no captive has ever had.

To the Aymaras of highland Bolivia, who in spite of their extreme poverty had steadily renounced fabulous wages in the mines or in the cities, the collecting of cinchona bark had become one of the main sources of livelihood which allowed them to remain in their cherished mountains. It had become in fact a family craft. The Jesuit missionaries had gone with the Aymaras into the forest and had taught them how to fell the tree in the proper way, how to strip its trunk, branches, and roots without wasting an inch of the priceless bark, how to store it in proper places and pack it conveniently for long journeys. More important still, they had taught them how to conserve and increase their patrimony by planting in the shape of the cross five trees for each tree they felled; and in attributing to this act some idea of divine protection the natives never neglected to do it.

When the exploitation of the cinchonas passed from the Jesuits to the government all these precautions slackened and the new generations of cascarilleros made great havoc in the cinchona forest. They peeled the tree only on the surface exposed after its fall, letting the rest rot in the ground, stored the bark in humid, unsuitable places, and, being of a more skeptical turn of mind than their ancestors, forgot to plant the five trees in the shape of the cross. This neglect was the more inexcusable since whenever the Indian cascarilleros came upon these plantings they never forgot to kneel down reverently and, hat in hand, say a prayer for the eternal rest of the souls of the *buenos padres*, those good fathers who in times long past had taught their people to care for the tree which mighty agencies now wanted to take away from them and which they intended to keep as they had kept their lands in the face of the far more devastating might of the Spanish conquistadors. This seeming carelessness which appeared to be leading to the rapid extermination of the trees had been greatly exaggerated, as those who believed the story were to discover to their dismay, and was the official reason for the universal concern for the calisayas. To save these trees from impending annihilation seeds from Bolivia were needed to start a plantation elsewhere, a procedure simple enough but obviously belonging to the category of the still simpler one devised by the mice in the old tale, of putting a bell on the cat in order to hear her approach: who was to put the bell on the cat?

In the region extending from northern Bolivia to southern Peru grows the forest of Caravaya, and it was ascertained that the calisaya grew abundantly in the Bolivian side of this forest. The boundaries at the time had not yet been properly defined and in fact a great deal of friction (both diplomatic and armed) was taking place between the two countries on this score. No wonder a traveler in the vicinity often found himself confused as to whether he was in Bolivian or Peruvian territory. On the assumption, therefore, that there may be as many ways of putting the bell on the cat as there are ways of skinning her, the forest of Caravaya became the theater of very curious proceedings.

About the year 1853 a foreign gentleman was seen wandering in and out of Caravaya. His demeanor was unconcerned and the sole purpose of his presence appeared to be merely the contemplation of natural beauty. In the year following, the mysterious traveler appeared on the Ides of March in the town of Sina, between Bolivia and Peru, where he made himself known as José Carlos Muller, as attested in a printed card he presented to the governor of the place by way of offering his respects. This ceremony concluded, Señor Muller proceeded to make certain proposals to the governor involving a great deal of money. They were immediately rejected. Fear more than honesty, however, had prompted this officer to his negativistic attitude, for he introduced to the foreigner a dubious character named Henriquez, also a stranger to the place though a Bolivian by nationality, who agreed to the proposals; whereupon Henriquez set forth into the forest of Caravaya and Mr. Muller departed for Sandia, a town definitely located in Peruvian territory, to settle down at his leisure.

In the month of June Henriquez joined Muller in Sandia and delivered to him four hundred plants of young calisaya trees. The possessor of a considerable sum of money, Señor Henriquez thereafter retired to a city in Bolivia, never again to grace Caravaya with his presence, which was just as well, since the people there had sworn to cut off both his feet on the first available occasion. Mr. Muller, on the other hand, managed with great difficulty to drag his plants along one hundred and fifty miles of jungle path to Arequipa and from there to the port of Callao in Peru, where a frigate with the regal name of *Prins Frederik der Nederlanden* took him on board with his booty.

José Carlos Muller reached Java in December 1854 and on his arrival, metamorphosis having occurred on the high seas, he landed in Batavia as Justus Charles Hasskarl, superintendent of gardens in Java. Mr. Hasskarl was made knight of the Netherlands Lion and commander of the Order of the Oaken Crown and was named director of the cinchona plantations about to be started.

No doubt the superintendent deserved all these honors and distinctions but in its elation the Dutch Government made the old mistake of counting its chicks before they hatched. All but two of the calisayas had died en route and, although Hasskarl had stocked himself with a good supply of seeds of another variety of cinchona, he made so unfortunate a choice for the site of the plantation that a year later the remaining trees were in a hopeless condition.

After this failure the Dutch were ready to dismiss the whole project, but Mr. Charles Pahud, governor general of the Netherlands East Indies, had set his heart on the plantations. After obtaining with great pains the means for their continuance, in 1856 he relieved Mr. Hasskarl of his duties and put Dr. Franz Junghuhn, a very able botanist, in his place. Collaborating with him was an excellent chemist named Dr. de Vrij, in charge of analyzing the quinine content of the barks. Junghuhn's first provision was to move the trees to a more favorable location, in the Malabar Mountains, a very costly and delicate operation which proved to be successful; four years later he had grown nearly a million trees in perfect blooming health. Except for a few thousand calisayas, these plants all came from the seeds collected by Hasskarl, and when De Vrij undertook the analysis of the barks he found that there was hardly a trace of quinine. Hasskarl had made a mistake and it was even questionable whether the tree was a cinchona at all. As for the calisayas, the descendants of those Hasskarl had brought presented a nondescript appearance, suggesting that Henriquez had been a man of unsuspected moral complexities. Only the few and none too robust offspring of Weddell's tree, by now a venerable relic, looked like real cinchonas. But their content in quinine was about half that of the calisaya barks from Bolivia, and it appeared that, although members of this family, they were not real calisayas. Thus by 1860 the Java experiment was a complete and dismal failure and had cost what in its day and age was a respectable fortune.

The government of British India meanwhile had long been considering the suitability of cinchona plantations, for quinine was needed in uncommonly large quantities there, and in spite of the disillusioning experience of the Dutch the government persisted in its intentions. The first attempt in this direction had been made in 1852, by way of a candid request from the Foreign Office to the British consuls in South America to obtain a supply of young plants and seeds of the various cinchonas. These worthy servants of the empire, however, try as they might, were unable to comply with the wishes of the Foreign Office, since the matter was not one to be transacted entirely by official channels, a situation which the Foreign

Office did not fully grasp until eight years later, when a British botanical expedition was sent to South America in search of the needed seeds and young plants.

The instigator, organizer, and leader of this expedition was Mr., later Sir, Clements Markham, who became famous through his manifold activities and interests as a historian, naturalist, explorer, geographer, and man of letters. To avoid Hasskarl's mistakes, which he erroneously attributed to incompetence, Markham had engaged to accompany him three expert botanists whose unquestionable ability was nevertheless of dubious value since the natural history of the cinchonas, far from completed to this day, is in itself a branch of botanical learning. Also contrary to Hasskarl's tactics, Markham openly stated the nature of his mission on the ground that no nation had the right to deprive others of a medicinal plant; that if the Old World had contributed to the New such priceless gifts as wheat, barley, rice, sheep, cattle, and horses it was most unfair that the New World should now deny to the Old a product of life-and-death importance; and that the South American governments could derive great advantages from the cultivation of the cinchonas in other countries by learning the results of the experiment without going to the considerable effort and expense it required. This hope Markham cherished since the welfare of the South American people was, according to his own statement, a subject of the deepest concern.

Markham was no doubt sincere in these arguments, which on first inspection sounded logical enough, although the suspicious mind might scent in them an undertone of sophistry, since the South Americans, far from depriving other nations of the drug, were only too eager to sell it—and always at a reasonable price, barring the interference of speculators. And if the Spaniards had introduced wheat, rice, barley, and such commodities into America they had come along themselves to benefit from them, whereas the South American people would in no way share in any benefit other nations might derive from their cinchona plantations. It is true that the South Americans could gain by the experience of others in the cultivation of the cinchonas and that Markham later on made considerable efforts to acquaint them with the results of the experiment in India, but it is also true that these advantages might be neutralized by the competition arising from the new plantations, which, should they be successful, would become most powerful, due to the surplus of cheap labor in overpopulated Java and British India. This possibility, however, was dismissed by Markham on the basis that, the need for quinine in the world being inconceivably great, any amount produced would have a ready market; and that if competition should lower its price, so much the better in view of the nature of the commodity in question. Yet this proved to be a gross miscalculation, for Markham had missed the fact that need has nothing to do with demand.

Markham with his helpers left for South America in December 1859 and returned some months later, his mission successfully accomplished. Again the forests of Caravaya became the theater of proceedings this time not so curious as violent in nature, for Markham had gone there personally with an expert attendant in search of the calisayas and very nearly lost his life in the enterprise, the people of Caravaya having kept very vividly in mind the Muller episode. Markham proved to be a very brave man; yet his expedition would have failed in its final objective if luck had not come to him in the person of a man who, though one of the great figures of his day, lived and died in obscurity.

To only a very few does the name of Richard Spruce suggest anything more than the well-known evergreen; he nevertheless did things that only a few men have done before or since, men like Aristotle, Von Humboldt, and Darwin. Though they had been honored and celebrated by their kind, Spruce was unrecognized. A Yorkshireman, Spruce was born in Gansthorpe in 1817 and became a master of mathematics at the age of twenty-two. He left the classroom to become a naturalist at twenty-seven and landed in South America in 1849 at the age of thirty-two, with the intention of exploring the region of the Amazon. This bold desire he gratified for some eight consecutive years, during which he traveled over ten thousand miles of river, collected thirty thousand botanical specimens, including seven thousand new flowering plants; gathered the most complete collection of mosses in the world, deserving of a six-hundred-page treatise; sent to the botanical gardens of Europe, particularly to the gardens of Kew, the most extraordinary collections of plant specimens; collected vocabularies of twenty-one Indian languages; and drew innumerable maps of regions so far unexplored. He also made the first botanical study of the rubber tree, thus providing for his countryman Wickham the scientific basis of one of history's great tragedies. Richard Spruce did all these things and more while navigating up and down the Amazon River and its various tributaries, coping with crocodiles, tropical storms, malaria, head-hunters, and murderous guides. Singlehanded and on his own he supported himself by selling collections of plant specimens, while dragging through the jungles a body so sick that, had it been inhabited by another spirit, it might never have risen from a hospital bed.

All his life Spruce had dreamed of some sort of position,

perhaps with a little salary, but particularly with a small office and a comfortable chair, where he could rest from his travels to study in peace and quiet his new plants; he never had it. He also considered the possibility of some consular appointment in South America, with perhaps a hundred and fifty pounds a year, enough to relieve him from the continuous drying and packing of specimens for sale; he never had that either, for want of powerful friends, he believed. Spruce in fact had never benefited from the blessings of an organized world; he was a self-taught botanist, a self-supported explorer, and a thoroughly ignored member of society until the day in 1858 when he received an official request from His Majesty's Secretary of State for India to provide Markham's party with plants and seeds of the cinchona tree of the variety known as the red by the color of its bark—to be compensated with a salary of thirty pounds a month for the duration of his services.

The red bark cinchona was a native of Ecuador, and Spruce was then in Peru. A three months' trip lay ahead of him across the Andes, through the region of the head-hunting Jivaros, where fourteen years before young D'Osery of Castelnau's expedition had vanished into thin air. Once in Ecuador, Spruce would have to climb the Chimborazo, one of the highest mountains in the Andes, the dead but ever menacing volcano that towers like a colossus over the beautiful valleys of Ecuador and on whose slopes grows the red bark cinchona.

It was a huge undertaking for any man, and for the ailing Spruce it proved to be disastrous. On his way to the Chimborazo he awoke one morning struck by a paralytic condition in his back and legs. "From that day forth," he wrote, "I was never able to sit up straight or to walk about without great pain and discomfort, soon passing to mortal exhaustion." Yet he dragged himself across torrents and up mountains until he saw what he later described as the most beautiful tree in the world (and Spruce had seen more trees than any man alive): the red bark cinchona with its height and shape in perfect harmony, its leaves shining bright, the young ones brilliant green and the old ones fiery red, making the slopes of the Chimborazo a regal carpet worthy of its own majesty.

The moment had arrived for the tedious work of collecting the seeds and rooting up the young trees. Spruce was terribly ill, feeling that "to lie down quietly and die would have seemed a relief"; yet he had to lie down far from quietly in an open bamboo shed, wrapped in clothes moldy from the fogs and dampness of the forest, which made his sleepless nights an inferno of physical pain and misery. Had Spruce listened attentively to the silence of the tropical forest he might have detected ominous whisperings, warning him not to do what he was prepared to do, telling him an old tale of sorrows that befell others for attempting what he was about to do, cautioning him that the gods of the forest had already laid their hand upon him; while the fogs that twisted and swirled in subtle contours in and out of his bamboo shed, the shadows taking the form of men long dead and now forgotten, went to hide behind the most beautiful tree Spruce had ever seen.

If such warnings were given to Spruce and if he heard them, as well he might (for the sick have special powers of perception), he did not heed them. The chance he had been waiting for all his life had come his way, the chance of obtaining the position that would give him the material comfort he needed so badly and the opportunity to develop the great work he had in mind: demonstrating in the evolution of plants a process parallel to that recently described by Darwin in the

animal species. Nothing could stop Spruce. Overcoming endless difficulties—civil war in Ecuador, lack of manual help, and
practically no means of transportation—with only one of
Markham's botanists to help him, Spruce, in constant agonizing
pain, gathered and sent in large numbers to the port of em-
barkation the required trees and seeds, all in excellent condition
due to his unsurpassed knowledge of tropical botany. His task
accomplished, however, all his expectations came to naught.
With the completion of his services the thirty pounds a month
ended and with it all hope of ever again enjoying such an
abundance. He became a helpless invalid at the age of forty-
three, but it was decreed that he should live to the age of
seventy-six, always in appalling physical suffering; the last
twenty years of his life were spent lying flat on his back.

The supply of trees and seeds reached India successfully in
1860. The plantations were immediately started in several
southern locations and it soon became apparent that Spruce's
red cinchona was the variety that thrived best. As for Markham's calisayas, they had all died en route. Eliminating practically all other varieties, emphasis was therefore put on the
cultivation of the red bark cinchonas, which bloomed and
reproduced themselves in the soil and climate of India with
remarkable ease and unbelievable rapidity.

Five years after the plantations were started nearly a million
trees had been distributed among private planters who obtained
the most amazing results in its cultivation, judging by the
following vivid description of the plantations in Ceylon:

Succirubra [red cinchona] is the variety in favour, the variety
in demand, the variety that pays, and the variety that thrives, requiring little attention in propagation, and costing next to nothing
to rear. It may be found growing luxuriantly everywhere, in the

mountain provinces, on fertile estates, and on the poorest patena soils, around Government rest-houses and remote police stations, in the various Kacheri grounds and gardens of Government residences; from the ancient kingdom of Kandy to the confines of the principality of Uvah. So familiar indeed has it become that it is looked upon as indigenous by both colonist and native, the latter having now the fullest confidence in it as a remedy, and not hesitating to help himself to a strip of bark from the nearest tree when occasion necessitates it.

Ceylon must have been a pretty sight under the bright green and red of the succirubras. By 1867 the government plantations covered twelve hundred acres and in this year the first India-grown barks were sold in the London market at rather profitable prices.

Meanwhile the Java plantations languished miserably. Dr. Junghuhn, whose capable efforts had resulted in the cultivation of a million worthless trees, died in 1864. His successor, Dr. van Gorkom, was making desperate efforts to save the plantations, which the government in Holland regarded as a most ill-fated enterprise. The Dutch residents in Java referred to it as the hobby of the governors general—a very extravagant hobby indeed, which the governor indulged in at the expense of the taxpayer. Eventually, in recognition of their pioneering efforts, the British supplied the Dutch with red bark cinchonas and these sturdy trees did as well in Java as they had in India.

But the red cinchona could not compensate the Dutch for the heavy losses already incurred in the plantations, since the red barks, when analyzed, appeared to be of a very special kind. It had been found that the cinchona bark contained besides quinine three other similar alkaloids named cinchonine, cinchonidine, and quinidine. In order to prepare pure sulphate of quinine these alkaloids were eliminated by chemical procedures, and what made the bark of the calisaya so desirable to the manufacturers was the fact that it contained quinine in much higher proportion than and almost to the exclusion of all the other alkaloids. The red cinchona, botanically known as *Cinchona succirubra*, contrary to the calisaya, contained the four alkaloids in almost equal proportions, with a total yield as high as eleven per cent, of which only about one fourth was quinine. The red bark from India and Java could therefore in no way compete with the calisaya bark from Bolivia in the European market, located in London, where the barks were auctioned to the manufacturers.

Thus the handsome red cinchona was a financial failure. But the search for the real calisaya was out of the question, as Bolivia was definitely forbidden ground and even the forests of Caravaya had become extremely dangerous territory. The truth of the matter, moreover, was that few had ever seen this extraordinary tree and the real calisaya seemed now like a dream, a mythical conception, a chimera as fabulous as the primeval forests of highland Bolivia where an ancient Indian nation, like some dragon of old, kept her pure and untouched by the kiss of the modern knights of industry. The only manifestation of its real existence was an incredible number of packs of bark that sold in the London market at preposterously high prices. Of its much publicized extinction no signs whatsoever had yet become evident.

It was believed that the three alkaloids other than quinine, so abundantly present in the red cinchona, also had antimalarial properties. This belief was strengthened by the fact that until 1820, when the procedure for isolating quinine was devised by Pelletier and Caventou, the cures that had made the bark famous had been effected by administering it whole as a powder, in which all the alkaloids existing in the bark were obviously present. In view of the results obtained from the red bark it was decided to study the question of whether the alkaloids other than quinine had any medical value.

For this purpose, three medical commissions were appointed in 1864 by the presidencies of Madras, Calcutta, and Bombay to report on the effectiveness of the three alkaloids as compared to quinine. The commissions started a series of carefully conducted investigations by administering each one of the alkaloids to a large number of malarial patients. After some three years of research they concluded that all were effective for the treatment of malaria, and that only in a matter of degree, or in individual cases, were they inferior to the pure sulphate of quinine, and that this inferiority in potency could easily be compensated by increasing the doses to be taken. This was an important medical contribution which also had its highly significant practical side, since a mixture of the four alkaloids could be manufactured more cheaply than the pure sulphate of quinine. Thus the humanitarian expectations that had prompted Markham in his questionable actions in South America would be fulfilled, since in his estimation the price of the drug had been "kept so high as to place this inestimable remedy beyond the means of millions of natives of fever-visited regions."

India was beyond doubt a fever-visited region, as proved by later statistics, which quoted one hundred million cases of malaria a year as a rather conservative estimate. A great chance now presented itself for the British to do for the people of India something that in times of reckoning would be infinitely to their credit. The government of British India, which also nursed in its bosom elements of the all-pervading and unpredictable liberalism of the nineteenth century, grasped at the chance with both hands. Government plantations were started in fourteen different locations and it was officially stated that they were a non-profit enterprise, their object being not to sell the cinchona barks at a profit in the London market for the European manufacturers but to supply the people of India with an anti-malarial febrifuge in the largest possible amounts at the lowest possible price.

To achieve this object, in 1866 the government of Madras secured the services of John Broughton, an eminent chemist from the Royal Institution, to experiment on the means of obtaining a febrifuge made of a mixture of all the alkaloids, "which would combine cheapness with efficacy in the highest degree," the goal being: "Every native druggist's shop in India should be supplied with this febrifuge remedy at the price of one rupee per ounce, and that thus fever should be comparatively banished from the land. . . ." By 1870 Broughton had completed his researches and was ready to start the manufacture of the febrifuge, for which purpose a factory was established under his direction in the Nedivattan plantations in Madras. According to Broughton's calculations, after all expenses were paid the febrifuge would be sold at one rupee per ounce. In the same year C. B. Clarke, superintendent of the Sikkim plantations in Bengal, began to experiment on the manufacture of a febrifuge similar to that of Broughton.

These were the first attempts to manufacture what later on became known as totaquine or "poor man's quinine." It was Spruce's gift to the world and a most appropriate one: quinine for the poor, for the native of Ceylon who helped himself to a strip of bark from the tree sent him by another pariah like himself.

The first botanist of his day, whose contributions to the science of natural history ranked with the greatest of any day, returned in 1864 to his country, consumed by disease, his entire resources consisting of twenty-seven pounds paid him by the British Government for a report on the cinchona forests of South America. And it was only through Markham's violent remonstrances and through the intercession of the Carlyle family that after much debating, arguing, and discussing whether the government should save Spruce from ending his days in a public institution, and if so whether the burden should fall upon the government of Britain or that of India, that a pension of fifty pounds a year was granted him by the Prime Minister, Lord Palmerston, very much in the spirit of unavoidable charity. It was not so bad after all, fifty pounds a year for a man whose ambition had been one hundred and fifty, and charity at least was something compared to the incomprehensible indifference with which Spruce always had been treated by his fellow men; fifty pounds a year to an invalid at the age of forty-seven was the first material reward in his life and a degree from the Imperial Academy of Germany the only honor ever bestowed upon him. Richard Spruce was simply a very unlucky man and his bad luck seems to have been of that awesome kind that touches everything connected with the victims it pursues. That poor man's quinine, Spruce's great practical contribution to mankind, was doomed to an end as grim as that of Spruce himself should have been no wonder.

At the time, however, the future seemed to be rosy for poor man's quinine. The crusading spirit having broken completely loose in the British camp, in an effort to spread the good deed trees and seeds were given to the Portuguese, who started plantations in the St. Thomas and Cape Verde islands, to the French, who tried the experiment in Indo-China, to Captain Maury from the United States to start plantations in Virginia, and to Emperor Maximilian, who wanted to do the same in Mexico, where quinine was very badly needed. Meanwhile the English themselves started plantations in the Mauritius Islands, the Fiji Islands, Jamaica, Reunion, Malay, and St. Helena; also in British Burma, with the purpose, as stated by His Grace the Duke of Argyll, Secretary of State for India, "that before many years the febrifuge will be within the reach of the people of all the higher hills of the Province."

The Indian experiment was the first attempt in contemporary times to carry on a public health campaign of national scope through government legislation. By 1870 it had been going on for ten years, during which a great deal of money and effort had been put into it; but the results now near at hand were most promising. The first deadly blow to the Hydra of the swamps was about to be struck.

CHAPTER XI

The Betrayal

When Charles Ledger left his native England to go to South America in 1836 he did not know that he would achieve immortality of a kind.

He was a trader and went to South America to buy things that he might promptly sell them, these things being mainly alpaca wool and cinchona bark. One gathers that he was a wholesome and likable person. In his dealings with the natives he seems not to have encountered any major difficulties nor in his business travels through the wilderness was he ever molested. What is still more surprising, he gathered around him a number of Indian servants, major-domos and the like, who attended to his interests most faithfully—and there is no better proof of a man's everyday virtues than the possession of honest and faithful servants. Ledger thus had done well in South America and by 1845 he was settled in the province of Puno in Peru as a respected and prosperous citizen.

Puno is adjacent to the Bolivian border, on the Peruvian side of Lake Titicaca, and when the value of the calisaya became known to its inhabitants they denounced as a monopoly Bolivia's determination to keep the calisaya for its own benefit and hopefully refused to believe that the tree would stop growing beyond man-created boundaries; and indeed nothing in the configuration or aspect of the terrain warranted such a belief. Thus, their eyes inevitably turned toward the forest of Caravaya, a group of citizens of Puno organized an expedition in 1845 to look for possible Peruvian calisayas. Charles Ledger was invited to join in this venture, contributing his part of the expenses with the prospect of sharing in the benefits. Every member of the expedition was to take with him a donkey and a servant. Ledger's servant was an Indian named Manuel Incra Mamani.

Manuel was a Bolivian and definitely an Indian of the highlands, for he possessed a knowledge of the cinchona tree that was absolutely phenomenal. He could detect at a glance differences between the various cinchonas, identical to anyone else; in fact he had pointed out to Ledger twenty-nine varieties, whereas Weddell in his celebrated book (and the best yet written on the subject) had described only nineteen. To Ledger, therefore, Manuel had been a godsend by virtue of his unerring eye in selecting the best quality barks from the lots offered for sale. Being from the highlands, Manuel was either an Aymara or a Quechua, or both, possibly with Spanish parentage; but, whatever he might be, he was one of the rare Indians of highland Bolivia who had left the native soil and, rarer still, had become the servant of a foreigner.

The expeditionary party from Puno left for Caravaya in high spirits and "the hope of making rapid fortune," to return two months later a crestfallen group. They had seen cinchonas in profusion, and numberless calisayas, in appearance exactly like those in Bolivia; but they knew, probably on Manuel's authority, that these were not legitimate calisayas. Though disappointing, the whole undertaking seems to have been a rather exciting and gaily conducted affair, since material failures seldom interfere with the Spanish capacity for momentary enjoyment.

Ledger returned to his trading with Manuel always on his heels. Ledger on his mule and Manuel on foot combed the countryside at the rate of some fifty miles a day, buying alpaca wool and cinchona bark. Manuel, inexorably expert, presided over these transactions. And as the years went by Ledger found in him the friend every man longs for and very rarely finds, perhaps because he seldom deserves it. In return Manuel was the recipient of his master's complete confidence. Once when Ledger was away on one of his business journeys his wife, uncertain where he was, had to send him important letters and money, for which task she called without hesitation upon Manuel. With sixty-five pieces of gold done up in his long hair, which made his person a very poor risk, Manuel traveled on foot seven hundred miles until he found Ledger. It had been a thirty-two-day journey, ample time to ponder on what to him was a great fortune, and on the fact that he could never be found should he choose to disappear.

About 1851 Ledger again became involved in some kind of project for finding the calisaya. It is not very clear how things were organized this time but it appears that another Englishman named George Backhouse was one of Ledger's associates. Whatever the arrangements may have been, one day Ledger received word from Backhouse that after having gone alone quite a distance into a part vaguely described as the *monte* he had found a *mancha* or patch of trees of the legitimate calisaya and was keeping watch by it, all of which clearly suggested that Backhouse had risked his way into Bolivian territory.

Ledger promptly sent him "money, knives, axes, beads and calicoes," but when the party reached the camp Backhouse was dead, his belongings stolen, and a pile of bark he had collected completely destroyed. Ledger records phlegmatically that wild

Indians murdered him, and the fact that these curious savages had indulged afterward in the destruction of the bark seems to have given him no clue as to the real motive for the murder. Ledger's messengers gave no account of the patch of real calisayas reported by Backhouse, which should have been very near his camp, but they were probably in a great hurry to leave the gruesome scene, made more sinister by the beads and calicoes they had so cheerfully brought. Ledger must have been reading books of adventure if after fifteen years of living among real Indians he still remained sentimental Englishman enough to believe in storybook natives who, free from white men's greed, gave fabulous treasures for a shaving mirror. Beads and calicoes for the Indians of highland Bolivia would really have been ludicrous if the solemn quality of these people had not made it an insult they did not deserve.

Backhouse's unpleasant end seems to have cured Ledger, at least temporarily, of any desire to look for the calisaya. He turned to other interests and in 1858 he performed the rather impressive feat of transporting a flock of alpacas from the Andean mountains to Australia, where unhappily the animals did not long survive. Having failed in the ambitious project of introducing the alpacas into another continent, he returned to Puno, where temptation beset him again. In 1861 he heard of Markham's party having reached South America in search of the cinchonas and this made him acutely aware of the wonderful opportunity to present Markham with calisaya seeds—at the proper price of course. This time Ledger decided on the direct approach and sent his overseer, a very capable Indian who had already been in his service nine years, to Bolivia with instructions to get the seeds. By what means the overseer was to accomplish his mission has not been recorded, but it does

not matter much because the story, by now wearisome, repeated itself and the overseer was presently murdered.

This was the third time in sixteen years that Ledger had attempted to get at the calisaya; and in all these years the competent Manuel, who knew so much about the cinchonas, seems
to have been curiously silent in regard to his master's repeated
failures. Yet there must have been something puzzling in Manuel's attitude that prompted a curious scene between master
and servant. One night, Ledger records, as the two were standing guard together, Ledger suddenly asked: "Do you think
we shall find the true bark?" To which Manuel quickly replied: "No, señor, the trees hereabouts do not see the snow-
capped mountains." Ledger nearly burst into laughter; and
yet, unexpected as the answer was, it is difficult to believe that
he could have felt like laughing.

If anybody had a right to laugh it was Manuel. For two
hundred years the educated of the world had steadily failed
in their attempts to learn something about the fever bark tree,
and when they finally laid their hands upon it they had blun-
dered throughout in trying to take it away from Manuel's
people. Meanwhile Manuel, and his people before him, had
known all about the fever bark tree. That this knowledge was
expressed in symbolic and rather beautiful terms was hardly a
matter for laughter. Manuel's explanation of the phenomenon
was a perfectly valid, empirical observation in the absence of
better knowledge. As is often the case, man-created boundaries
follow geographical accidents, in this instance some particularly deep valley whence the Andean tops could not be seen,
and it was on climbing toward Bolivia that the real calisayas
were found, as the snowy peaks of the cordilleras began to
appear on the horizon. Controlling his ill-timed impulse to

hilarity, Ledger seems to have realized all of this because, later on in his bed, he pondered long into the night on Manuel's answer to his question.

In 1861, after eighteen years of unfailing devotion, Manuel left Ledger's service and went back to his native Bolivia, where he hired himself as a cascarillero. Four years later he was still there collecting bark but in the winter of that year he stealthily undertook a long and perilous journey. From La Paz, the capital of Bolivia, he started on foot across the Andes, facing terrible odds. He would have to brave unbearably cold weather at high altitudes and find his way in blinding snowstorms along mountain paths so narrow that, should he meet another traveler, they could hardly pass each other. Or he might not find his way at all because the continuous earthquakes in those mountains had an uncanny way of making the landscape unrecognizable by erasing familiar trails. To undertake such a voyage in the middle of winter was suicidal, as evidenced by the frozen bodies so often found in those parts, the sight of which made the lonely traveler the victim of fearsome hallucinations since, being in a perfect state of preservation, they were truly the most unearthly of apparitions. But Manuel had to travel in midwinter because it was the season of the year when the rains halted the collecting of bark, and he did not want his absence to be noticed. Otherwise there was a good chance that someone might overtake him and make it impossible for him to reach his destination, which was Tacna in Peru. He managed to arrive there safe and sane after a march of eight hundred miles, during which in all probability he had made no stops other than to say a prayer whenever he came upon five trees planted in the shape of the cross.

After a separation of four years Manuel the servant met his

former master in Tacna and presented him with a small and precious package that he had carried all the great distance, probably hidden in his long braids in which he took so much pride. And well he might, for in addition to being ornamental they had stood him in good stead as a secret hiding place for this package, even as they had done years previously for the far less dangerous and valuable cargo of sixty-five pieces of gold. Not only were the seeds contained in this package from the real and legitimate calisaya but they were from the best specimens within this select family, a patch of fifty calisayas Manuel had patiently looked for and found in so inaccessible a location that no botanist in the world would ever have discovered them. And even if he had, he would never have guessed their superiority, which Manuel recognized by a slight difference in the coloring of the leaves, and because they looked out upon the snow-capped tops of the Andes Mountains in all their glory. The seeds, after being properly dried, were put in a small box, wrapped up in a hide, and sent by Ledger to England, where his brother George was to carry on the negotiations conducive to their sale to the government for the plantations in British India.

In recompense for Manuel's four years in Bolivia Ledger gave him a hundred and fifty pounds. But Manuel had not betrayed his people for money, for he could have stolen from Ledger many times the amount given him and every man knows instinctively that theft is a lesser crime than treason. Manuel betrayed his people for love of the master who had been kind to him; the master, in fact, whom he, Manuel, had been protecting for over twenty-two years. After watching this helpless master trying time and again to get what Manuel knew he never would get, Manuel gave it to him, which was easy enough for him, since it was his. Whether during all these years Ledger had consciously and deliberately driven Manuel to this decision we shall never know.

His money received, Manuel retraced the eight hundred miles across the Andes back to Bolivia: an incredibly insane thing to do and rendered doubly so because he went back with the purpose of getting more seeds for Ledger. Again he braved the unbearable cold, the storms, the dangerous trails, the tropical forests on the lower levels, the awesome solitude of nature, nowhere so overpowering as in those cordilleras of the Andes, where the Indian gods had dwelt for so long, undisturbed by human company. Up the mountains crawled the little man who had committed treachery to face alone the gods of his ancestors, who could crush him to dust. But they would not; for him and for his lowly actions they felt only the contemptuous amusement they felt for the chaotic behavior of all men as compared to the orderly intelligence that ruled the world of nature, over which they preside. Consistent with its harmonious ways, nature had provided the remedy for one of mankind's greater curses, as it would provide the remedy for many other of man's ills if only he knew how to look for it. It had been solely through the curious workings of man that the remedy had been kept away from those who needed it. Now the remedy was taken away from the Indian forests. But the gods let it go because they knew that the little men who had stolen it would, because of their incompetence, lose it and one day have to come back for it. And the gods of the forest shook with Homeric laughter at the limitless incapacity of man to use for his own advantage the magnificence of creation.

Thus Manuel was allowed to return to Bolivia to his unavoidable fate, knowing that the Aymaras of the highlands, who sold their children rather than their land, would never forgive him for what he had done but would surely reach him no matter where he might go.

It was not until five years later, in 1870, that Ledger had news of him through Manuel's son, who went to see Ledger to account for money the latter had sent to his father. Manuel of course was dead. He had been put in jail and, in a fruitless attempt to force him to tell for whom he had stolen the seeds, he was beaten and starved for twenty days, after which he was set free to die, his jailers probably wanting to save themselves the trouble of burying him. Manuel's son, who must have grown up in Ledger's household, because by now it was thirty years since his father had entered the Englishman's service, offered to get more seeds for him. Ledger flatly refused the offer. Manuel Incra Mamani was the last victim of the fever bark tree. The fight was now over; but those who had scored the final victory would have missed it, had not chance come to their rescue.

When George Ledger offered the box of seeds for sale he found no buyer. The government of British India showed no interest in the offer. Markham, who might have realized the unique value of the seeds, was somewhere abroad. Fearing that they might deteriorate, George Ledger offered the seeds to the Dutch Government, which also reacted somewhat indifferently to the proposal, though willing to enter into negotiations. It was not until after much corresponding and bargaining that the seeds were finally sold, half to a private planter in India and half to the Dutch Government, which paid one hundred gulden for their share with the understanding that if the seeds were in good condition Ledger would be further compensated. When the small box reached Java in 1866 and was opened the smell of decay was so strong that it seemed as though the seeds must be completely rotten.

But they were not; they germinated without difficulty and Charles Ledger received five hundred more gulden. About the time he learned of Manuel's death the good news came from Java that the legitimate calisaya, with the highest quinine content, was being successfully raised. The fate common to all traitors befalling Manuel, that no recognition comes to them even from those who benefit from their misdeeds, it was decided that the new tree was to be officially classified as the *Cinchona ledgeriana*. The only effort toward an obituary in Manuel's memory was a rather perplexing commentary from Markham: "It is a sad story," he wrote, "but at the same time it is very pleasant to have to record these noble traits of character in the Indians."

Thus it was that Charles Ledger achieved immortality of a kind, and the wild Indians of the forest finally lost their tree.

CHAPTER XII

Rich Man's Quinine

In 1873 the superintendent of the government plantations in Java wrote the following:

As soon as the excellent quality of Ledger's Cinchona was known to us . . . Mr. Van Gorkom at once resolved to discontinue the culture of all other Cinchonas . . . to cut all the now existing trees as soon as they are fit to give a good bark crop, and when their place can be taken by Ledgerianas. The greater part of the seedlings and cuttings of our old Calisayas that still remained in the propagating houses and nurseries, were thrown away and Ledgerianas propagated as fast as possible. . . . There are at present 40,000 young Ledgerianas. . . . Let us hope . . . we can bring every year a great quantity of Ledger's bark in the market and so make quinine much cheaper than it is now. . . .

In 1874 he wrote again: "In a few years we shall have upwards of two million trees of this superior species."

How superior the ledgeriana was can be judged by the fact that its quinine content could be as high as thirteen per cent, while before its introduction a cinchona yielding from one to one and a half per cent was considered a tree worthy of preservation. Moreover the quinine of the ledgeriana, being almost free of any of the other alkaloids, was very easily made into quinine sulphate, an advantage of primary importance for the manufacturers. Thus, in an auction held in Amsterdam in 1877, the ledgeriana barks sold at 17.58 florins per kilogram, the red barks at 3.36 florins per kilogram. The Java plantations were saved.

Twenty-six years had passed since Hasskarl had left for South America to get cinchona trees and the Java experiment had begun. For twenty-six years, then, the Dutch government had lavished untold amounts of money on a seemingly hopeless enterprise. That after twenty years of consecutive failures they would undertake to experiment anew with the ledgeriana was in itself a remarkable instance of perseverance, for they could not foresee in the least the amazing results which came at long last—and not the easy way. Although the ledgeriana was a sturdier tree than the other calisayas it was far from being as strong as the red cinchona. In fact it requires the most meticulous care. It is easily attacked by disease, and it took a careful process of selection and elimination to obtain a number of fairly resistant ledgerianas with a more or less uniform quinine content. The final success of these trees required that some of the best botanists and chemists of the day, provided with excellent laboratories and experimental stations, should devote themselves for several years to one of the most important botanical experiments ever accomplished. But from now on both government and scientific staff were to play second fiddle. The Dutch colonists in Java, who had regarded the cinchona experiment as the hobby of the governors general, were now eager to embark on its cultivation. Beginning in 1867, the government helped private planters to get started by giving them seeds and expert advice and in no time the private plantations were thriving.

Needless to say, the success of the ledgeriana in Java was a sore blow to the private planters in India. The red barks, so abundant there, could no longer be sold profitably in the European market and the native market was supplied by the government plantations, against which there was no possible competition. Thus in 1870 the Darjeeling Cinchona Association of private planters in Bengal presented a request that the government should either limit the extent of its plantations or buy the private ones, which the members of the association were willing to relinquish at a loss by accepting the government's own price. The Duke of Argyll, Secretary of State for India, replied: "The supply of ordinary barks is practically unlimited from South America . . . and the efforts of Cinchona cultivators in India, who merely undertake the work as a commercial speculation, should be turned to the production of barks having the richest yield of crystallizable quinine." This was sound advice but the bark with the richest yield of crystallizable quinine came from the ledgeriana, which did not survive in India. The soil and climate of India so favorable to the red cinchona proved to be inadequate for its more aristocratic relative and the ledgerianas, becoming the prey of all sorts of diseases, eventually died out.

Again in 1871 the Darjeeling Association repeated its request and again offered its plantations for sale. The Government Cinchona Commission, refusing to consider the matter further, answered through Hume, Secretary of the Government of British India, that the government, which had given all kinds of help to the private planters, was willing to continue to do so but "Government feels," added the Secretary, "that it could not, without the abnegation of a vitally important duty, leave solely to private enterprise the further prosecution of those measures necessary to secure to the people . . . the only efficient specific for the most deadly of all Indian maladies." In accordance with Hume, the Duke of Argyll agreed that "the encouragement of private enterprise . . . must always be looked upon as subordinate to the main object of Her Majesty's Government . . . in having undertaken the introduction of Cinchona cultivation into India."

In pursuance of this main object the anti-malarial febrifuge, based on a mixture of all alkaloids, was being manufactured very successfully in Madras by Broughton. In 1873 the factory produced two hundred and forty-five pounds of the drug and it was most effective for the treatment of fevers, as reported by the Surgeon General of Hospitals, who strongly recommended its production in large quantities at the price of one rupee per ounce.

Clarke, in the Bengal factory, had not been so successful and, after accepting his resignation, in 1872, the government of India requested from the Secretary of State that a quinologist from England be sent to Bengal to take charge of the manufacture of the febrifuge. According to the official request, ". . . the gentleman selected should be a person of undoubted scientific eminence as an analytical chemist, versed, if possible, in the specialties of the European methods . . . and certainly possessed of such high general intelligence as to enable him . . . to master readily the complex conditions he will have to deal with . . ." since, proceeded the request, "to arrest the deadly ravages of the low fevers prevalent throughout India, even to palliate the suffering and misery that they yearly entail on millions of the population, it is not sufficient merely to make quinine; it is absolutely necessary to make it in enormous quantities and at a very low price." The salary offered was six hundred pounds a year, to be increased one hundred pounds yearly until it reached twelve hundred a year, and the Indian Government hoped that ". . . the scientific direction of a great and important manufacture, and the prosecution of interesting scientific researches, is of a nature to attract even the most eminent among the rising men of science." This was indeed a handsome offer, such as very seldom comes the way of rising men of science, and showed that the Indian Government was intent on carrying out its philanthropic enterprises in the proper manner.

In 1873, C. H. Wood, a highly recommended chemist, went to Bengal to organize the manufacture of the febrifuge in the Sikkim plantations. In a preliminary report discussing the advisability of selling the febrifuge at one rupee per ounce, Wood again emphasized the plight of the private planters by suggesting that the government "would not wish to sell their alkaloid in the bazaars, excepting at such a reasonable price as would admit of private planters competing with them. . . ." In which case the alkaloid would cost the same as in the market and there was no point in making it in India. Wood implied that there was no point either in cultivating the red bark, since there was no demand for it in London, and that the plantations should concentrate on the cultivation of the calisayas.

At this report Lord Salisbury, who had succeeded the Duke of Argyll as Secretary of State for India, seems to have flown into a rather un-British temper: "The question for . . . Wood to consider," he answered, "is not what kind of bark fetches the highest price in the London market. . . . I desire, therefore, that the officers in charge of the Cinchona cultivation, may be instructed that their aim should not be to grow the largest amount of Quinine-yielding barks simply, but to grow the bark yielding the largest percentage of febrifuge alkaloids generally. . . . It should be understood that the object of Cinchona cultivation . . . is not a commercial speculation." His lordship was promptly reassured that the red barks were given the proper consideration, and in 1874 Wood made, with excellent results, the first large-scale tests of his febrifuge, which commanded high praise from the Surgeon General and could be sold at one rupee per ounce.

Meanwhile the position of the private planters was becoming increasingly difficult. This was not because of government competition, as they had at one time imagined, but because of the failure of the ledgeriana in India. This fact had also escaped the government when Secretary Hume refused to consider the proposals of the Darjeeling Association, saying that unfortunately the number of malarial patients was so enormous that neither government nor private individuals nor both, no matter how hard they tried, could possibly hamper each other. How enormous was the number of malarial patients Secretary Hume never knew; but their complete indigence made them of no value to private planters, who were trying to make a living. What market there was among the well to do was already being usurped by the planters from Java by virtue of the high quality of their bark.

The superiority of the ledgeriana was becoming more and more evident, to the point that it could compensate for the elaborate process of its cultivation. This began with the selection of the seeds, an operation of great delicacy performed in a dark room by specially trained women who with birds' feathers separated the seeds spread out on glass lighted from below. The selected seeds were then planted in nurseries in virgin soil brought from the forests. The young plants were kept for six months at a constant temperature, with continuous moisture maintained by thin sprayers, and were covered with cotton material soaked in oil to let the light through. They

were afterward transplanted to other nurseries to be kept for
eighteen months under constant supervision, after which time
they were planted in the open and during the next year, by a
process of survival of the fittest, a number of weak trees had
to be rejected. The survivors were finally transplanted, with
the earth around them, to the regular plantations.

Then the danger of disease began. The roots are very sensi-
tive to some dangerous form of cancer that spreads under-
ground, and when a tree is attacked by this ailment it has to be
rooted up without leaving a trace of the diseased root, while
not disturbing the roots of neighboring trees. This problem
was partly solved by grafting the ledgeriana on the roots of the
red cinchona, which can stand anything. It is no wonder that
the superintendent in Java wistfully remarked: "The culture
of succirubra is very seducing, as it is so exceedingly easy."

Seven or eight years later the quinine content, which regu-
lates the price of the bark, reaches its peak; this varies according to the years and even in the ledgeriana can be as low as
from three to four per cent. The tree is then felled or rooted
up, since after much experimentation it was found that the
greatly decried felling of the trees in South America was inevitable because they would die anyway when stripped of their
bark. Women carefully peel trunk, branches, and roots. The
bark is afterward dried in hot-air ovens at constant temperature, powdered, and shipped to Amsterdam. Thus every ten
to twenty-five years the whole plantation is rooted up, the soil
has to be thoroughly cleansed and, being completely exhausted,
has to be carefully enriched.

Only in the very exceptional conditions that existed in Java
could this elaborate process, involving for several years a capital investment without return, become a profitable undertak-

ing: lands were practically free, taxes low, and there was a surplus of labor not only cheap but uncommonly skillful. Java produced the best though obviously the most expensive cinchona barks in the world. Competition as to quality being out of the question, both the South American and Indian barks had to give way to the ledgeriana. In 1881 South America had exported over nine million kilograms of bark and by 1884 this amount had already been reduced to about two million. As London had replaced Rome, now Amsterdam replaced London as the cinchona market. Here again the renowned housekeeping efficiency of the Dutch proved to be unsurpassed. The first public auction of ledgeriana bark was held in Amsterdam in 1869, and from 1888 on ten auctions a year were held, all carefully planned, with excellent storage facilities provided, catalogues sent to the buyers, and samples of the bark distributed for analysis.

All this could not but increase the price of the bark, which had then to be manufactured into sulphate of quinine. In this respect, however, the Dutch had to surrender supremacy to the Germans, who in their excellently equipped chemical firms staffed by highly trained personnel very soon made the best sulphate of quinine, a high quality product of unrivaled purity. But this product in relation to the problem of malaria was no more available than is a Rolls-Royce as a general means of transportation. After this brief outline of the evolution of the drug from seed to tablet, it is a platitude to say that sulphate of quinine as manufactured in Europe from the barks of Java could be anything but rich man's quinine. It had its market, as does a Rolls-Royce, and thus reached only a very small percentage of the world's malarial population.

For the remaining millions of victims the solution was the

Indian-manufactured mixture of alkaloids, which now had become poor man's quinine. But poverty in the great malarial areas being abject, poor man's quinine became a philanthropic proposition. As a commercial commodity it had no value. The mixture of alkaloids from India and also from Java, where several attempts were made to produce it, appeared to be of "variable composition," the proportion of the different alkaloids changing in relation to each other in each batch of the remedy. This did not detract from its curative virtues but made its administration less of a routine matter than that of sulphate of quinine, which was of constant composition.

One may speculate whether, if the ledgeriana had not succeeded in Java, efforts would have been intensified to perfect the manufacturing methods of totaquine. After all, poor man's quinine had once been rich man's quinine when Sir Robert Talbor had cured the kings of Europe with a crude extract of cinchona bark compared to which the febrifuge made in India was a highly refined product. This question, however, was settled the day Manuel Mamani crossed the Andes from Bolivia to Peru with a package of seeds.

As the production of ledgeriana increased, the private planters in India faced ruin. In 1876 a private planter with two thousand acres was the first to root up the red cinchona; the land was sold in blocks for the "more successful culture of tea." This process continued, though not fast enough, for in the eighties the market was flooded by bark. In 1887 Ceylon alone produced thirteen million pounds of red bark; and thus came the quinine crash. The private plantations in India were dismantled and tea was planted instead of cinchona. Discontinued also were the plantations in the Mauritius Islands, the Fiji Islands, Jamaica, St. Helena, Reunion, and Malay, the

Portuguese plantation in the St. Thomas and Cape Verde islands, and the French in Indo-China.

The plantations in Java survived, though their position was very precarious and remained so for several years until the surplus bark, enormously increased by the peeling of millions of trees that had been uprooted, began to subside. Nobody wanted the millions and millions of pounds of bark which might have saved the lives of millions of people.

The government plantations in British India managed to survive the blow that shattered all hope of compensating for free and cost-price distribution of the drug by selling bark in the European market. The government of British India might have saved the private plantations by buying them. Yet in spite of the little care required by the red cinchona, the extent of the private plantations probably made the enterprise beyond the scope of a single government. Some sort of international organization might have been able to maintain them, but at the end of the nineteenth century this was hardly feasible.

In fact we should rather wonder that the government plantations managed to survive at all and have remained to this day. Several thousand pounds of the anti-malarial febrifuge are distributed at reduced price every year in India. A few thousand more are given free, since a rupee per ounce proved to be too high a price, and some ten million cases of malaria are treated annually in the public dispensaries. Viewing the problem of malaria in India as a whole, this is a mere drop in the bucket; but factories and plantations are there, and someday, if totaquine has not been superseded by a cheaper and better drug, they may be expanded to meet the general needs.

The express desire to secure "for the fever-stricken millions of India the inestimable blessing of cheap quinine" will be attained and it will be a monument to the memory of a group of gallant men, like the Duke of Argyll, Lord Salisbury, Secretary Hume, who belonged to a generation undeservedly slighted as pompous and exacting old Victorians.

CHAPTER XIII

Hercules, the Hydra, and
the Birds

When this energetic century of ours came into being it gave no outward signs of the internal malformations that very shortly were to result in a unique display of collective dementia. The century in fact began gaily enough and its first decade was the culmination of an era in which individual ingenuity and resourcefulness had reached unprecedented attainment. It was the end of an agelong struggle against medieval terrors and uncompromising beliefs, and the occidental man was once again the Roman citizen who could allow all gods and accept all philosophies so long as they did not interfere with such things as the water supply of the city of Rome.

The barriers broke for a fleeting moment; the new aristocracy of wealth appeared hand in hand with the old aristocracy of the blood; the merchant baron and the industrial grandee, together with the prince and the grand duke with names as old as history itself, made a public appearance of great magnificence. The great capitals of Europe presented a sight of unparalleled splendor. Passports were non-existent and gold was the universal currency; political exiles were a rare and colorful occurrence. Enrico Caruso was the most courted man of the day. The opening night at the opera in Vienna, the Grand Prix at Auteuil, the jewels of Queen Alexandra, the regatta at Kiel, the first ball of the season given by Princess

Yussupoff in St. Petersburg, or the wedding of a Rothschild were occasions never to be forgotten.

Meanwhile things were happening, and happening fast. Populations were shifting from rural to industrial areas, technical improvements were increasing production beyond the pace of demand, an army of specialized city labor was being created which if unemployed would become an insoluble problem, public health service was to double the average span of life. As a result of these happenings great changes began to take place; perhaps the most important in its final effects was the replacement of the individual by the institution. The era of committees, agencies, commissions, boards, and councils was beginning and with it the avoidance of individual responsibility and the deprivation of individual fulfillment. Frustration was to become the great disease of the day, with hero worship its logical accompaniment; millions of thwarted people would identify themselves with one exalted leader and bring about the era of dictatorships.

The history of the fever bark tree is a good example of this suppression of the individual. Until the end of the nineteenth century every phase in the history of this tree, every decision for or against its use, on which depended the destinies of millions of people, had been decided by an individual. It was a well-meaning viceroy who seems to have brought the drug to Europe and a quixotic cardinal who decided to make it known. It was a learned as well as inept professor who threw it into disrepute, and it was an intelligent as well as daring charlatan who gave it back its reputation. And so the story proceeds with the development of the eastern plantations: the chance intervention of Spruce made those in India possible and the frailties of Manuel made those in Java profitable.

But with the arrival of the twentieth century the main characters in the history of cinchona are such entities as planters and manufacturers, with supply and demand the contributing factors, conditioned by markets, prices, currencies, and problems of distribution. From now on, no one is individually to be blamed for what happens to the cinchona tree and no one is individually to be praised.

The planters of Java, which became the world's source of bark for sulphate of quinine, had a very hard time. First they fought the Dutch Government on the ground that it offered unfair competition, and after 1874 they insisted that the government plantations should be limited to experimental stations. The government, on the other hand, felt that the benefits of so costly an experiment, financed by the whole community, should not be limited to a single group and the issue was finally solved when the government plantations became profit-making enterprises on equal terms with the private estates and thus offered no further unfair competition. The government plantations, however, reserved for themselves the right to sell to other nations planting material from their highly scientific nurseries.

This battle won, the planters were faced with the manufacturers. After 1880 the first modern factories of sulphate of quinine were established and by 1892 the manufacturers had created a syndicate or trust under the direction of the German manufacturers, who soon were to produce half of the world's supply of quinine. This trust was organized with the understanding that the manufacturers would not outbid each other for the bark and would avoid competition by all selling quinine at the same price. Thus the price of the bark was kept low while the price of quinine was kept high, and there was nothing the planters could do, since they could sell only to the manufacturers' trust.

In 1896 the planters, faced with the possibility of having to discontinue the cultivation of cinchona, decided to manufacture their own quinine from their own bark. For this purpose a factory was established in Bandoeng, Java, where the bark was processed on commission for the planters, who afterward undertook to sell the drug. By 1898 the Bandoeng factory produced some hundred kilograms of quinine a day. Immediately the price of bark doubled in Amsterdam and the majority of planters, preferring to make their profit directly on the bark, again sent it to Amsterdam instead of having it processed at the Bandoeng factory. The factory could have continued in business, but the European manufacturers, with their larger stock, dumped quinine on the market, and by 1901 had forced the planters to abandon altogether the manufacture of the drug. In 1905 the Bandoeng factory had joined the trust of manufacturers. The price of bark, which in 1895 had been 2.93 cents a unit and which by virtue of the competition offered by the Bandoeng factory had gone up to 10 cents in 1900, was again down to 3.11 cents by 1911. After a twenty-year struggle the planters were right back where they had started, faced once more with the prospect of having to discontinue the cultivation of cinchona; and as the first step in this direction they began to curtail shipments of bark to Amsterdam.

By 1911, however, the position of the manufacturers had somewhat weakened. Industry, which in the nineteenth century had been a great adventure wherein many had met with ruin, had become by the twentieth century a fairly stable undertaking and the manufacture of sulphate of quinine for a limited market—that is, for the contingent of malarial patients who could afford an expensive drug—was a definitely good investment. The great agricultural enterprises, on the other hand, such as the elaborate cultivation of the ledgeriana, were full of uncertainties. Many a planter in Java might therefore be willing to exchange his plantation for a quinine factory, and cinchona plantations are not to be improvised. At this point the manufacturers decided to compromise with the planters.

Throughout the history of quinine, the word "monopoly" keeps recurring at every step. The Jesuits were the first to be accused of monopolistic practices, and the mystery that surrounded the fever bark tree for the first hundred years following the introduction of the drug was attributed to deliberate secrecy on the part of the Jesuits. Yet the accusation loses weight when it comes to the role played by the Jesuit Cardinal de Lugo. His efforts to make quinine known and available, in which he spent a considerable part of his personal fortune, were so evidently unquestionable that he is in fact the only major figure in the history of cinchona who remains above suspicion. There is testimony from one source that Sir Robert Talbor "cornered the market" on the drug to stop others from experimenting with it. The Spanish Crown attempted for several years to organize a state monopoly of the cinchona forests of South America. Bolivia's government did succeed on and off in controlling the exploitation of its calisaya forests.

The first successful attempt, however, toward monopolizing the drug took place in the United States. During the war in Florida against the Seminole Indians (1835–42) the military importance of quinine became apparent in the new republic; Surgeon C. McCormick instituted in the army the practice of its administration. When the Civil War broke out, the need for quinine was immediately felt and by the end of the war, according to the purveyor's report, nearly thirty tons of the drug had been sold to the government—at two dollars and ten cents an ounce at the beginning of the war and from then on at any price. And this did not take into account the quinine for the Confederate armies, which arrived safely as contraband of war, stored on one occasion in mattresses, and the price of which soared as high as fifteen dollars an ounce. Only two firms were in a position to supply the government with sulphate of quinine: first, because they were the only ones who manufactured it in the United States; and second, because there were no stocks in the country due to the fact that imported sulphate of quinine had a protective duty of forty-five per cent. After the Civil War this duty was reduced to twenty per cent. Popular opinion, however, was not satisfied and, decrying the duty as a "tax on blood," succeeded, mainly with the help of the New York *Tribune*, the foremost champion of high tariff in the United States, in having the tax repealed under the Dingley Act of 1897.

The American monopoly, having no control over the sources of quinine, could not affect other nations. Thus it was not until 1913, when the Java planters and the Association of Manufacturers reached an agreement known as the First Quinine Convention, that the real monopoly began to take shape. The Association included eleven factories—three German, four French, one English, two Dutch, and the Bandoeng factory in Java—and was under the administrative control of the Deutsche Gold- und Silberscheidenanstalt vorm. Roessler of Frankfort. After long and painful debate the agreement was signed between one hundred and twenty-two Java planters and seven manufacturers, to remain in effect from July 1913 to July 1918. The manufacturers were pledged to purchase a minimum of bark at a fixed price, the planters were to have a maximum of bark at their disposal, and the net profit from sulphate of quinine was to be divided, one third for the planters and the other two thirds for the manufacturers. The execution of the agreement was entrusted to the Kina Bureau in Amsterdam formed by seven members: three representing the planters, three the manufacturers, and one chairman having no interests whatsoever in the quinine industry.

This agreement became automatically void with the declaration of war in 1914. The long-awaited chance had come now, and the planters sold bark directly to all the belligerent nations. With the difficulties in shipping, the Bandoeng factory increased its production until by the end of the war it manufactured over three fourths of the world's total production of quinine. With the war quinine had become a priceless commodity, absolutely indispensable on the Eastern Front, and the world at large became aware of the danger of having the only steady source of quinine concentrated in a single spot on the globe, within the jurisdiction of a single nation. This prompted Mr. Herbert Hoover, Food Administrator, to send a concise as well as perplexing telegram to the Philippines, simply saying, "Raise quinine." When the Dutch Government was persuaded by the Allied governments to sign the War Agreement of September 3, 1918, whereby practically the whole production of bark was turned over to the Allies for the duration, both planters and the Bandoeng factory were forced to cancel their contracts with the Central Powers. An action of this kind could undoubtedly turn the tide of war and it should have been a very fair warning indeed.

The war ended, and in the ensuing optimism the problem of quinine was temporarily forgotten, as there were many other problems equally important. Thus no particular attention was paid to the fact that in July 1918 the planters and manufacturers had reached a new agreement known as the Second Quinine Convention. This time the only signatories on the part of the manufacturers were the Dutch factories: the Amsterdam Chinine Fabriek, the Nederlandsche Kinine Fabriek, and the Bandoeng factory; and on the part of the planters, the majority of the large ones with the exception of British- and Japanese-owned plantations, which controlled only ten per cent of the total bark production of Java. Thus ninety per cent of the Java bark, which represented eighty per cent of the world's total production, was to be sent to Amsterdam to be distributed by the Kina Bureau, which was now under the complete control of the Dutch manufacturers.

With its defeat in 1918 Germany lost control of the quinine industries as well as the cinchona plantations it had started in Africa about 1905; all of which was no minor matter, for quinine was the cornerstone upon which Germany meant to build her great colonial empire of the future. In an effort to make Germany independent of the Dutch, the I. G. Farbenindustrie must have begun very promptly its search for a synthetic anti-malarial.

The new quinine agreement followed the spirit of the old, with the difference that in order to obtain bark the foreign factories no longer had to be members but could be merely associates of the Kina Bureau, though they were still constrained to sell quinine at the price set by the Bureau. The planters, on the other hand, could not sell bark to anyone outside the Bureau without its permission and were pledged to keep the Bureau informed of their stocks and the extent of the plantation, as guaranty that they would produce the maximum amount of bark agreed upon, which as a rule exceeded the amount actually bought by the manufacturers. The Kina Bureau was endowed by all parties with the authority to apply sanctions, which in the case of the manufacturers was the refusal of bark, and fines in the case of the planters. In compensation for these restrictions the manufacturers were assured of a steady supply of bark of the quality desired, and the planters could count on a steady outlet for their bark at a profit. Thus the production, distribution, and price of quinine became ironbound and through the offices of the Kina Bureau the quinine industry avoided the hazards of demand and competition.

In spite of these advantages the Kina Bureau was not a popular organization, either inside or outside the quinine industry. It was accused of keeping the price high and the supply low by avoiding competition. To this the Bureau answered that the price would be much higher if the drug should fall into the hands of speculators, who would make the supply not low but definitely uncertain. The Bureau claimed, moreover, that it was always ready to increase the production of quinine at a moment's notice and that at all times the supply exceeded the demand, regardless of the price, so that the quinine industry was always threatened with a surplus. This was particularly true after 1921 when, due to the decrease in buying power all over the world, the demand for quinine diminished considerably, although the price which in 1914 had been twenty florins a kilogram and had gone up to fifty-two florins in 1920 due to the war demand, was down to thirty-five florins by 1924.

Thus in 1923 it was decided that the amount of bark to be delivered to the Kina Bureau was to be fixed each year according to the previous year's demand. This again placed the planters at the wrong end of the bargain, and in 1927 they formed the Association of Cinchona Bark Producers, joined by the government plantations, which therefore also joined the Kina Bureau although "retaining the right to resign therefrom on one year's notice should it be of opinion that the Cinchona Agreement is an obstruction to providing malarial regions with cheap Quinine." On renewing the agreement in 1928 it was decided that the planters could reduce the acreage of their plantations year by year. In 1929 the Association of Bark Producers in Java organized a campaign to limit the production of bark, and it encouraged planters to retire by purchasing their plantations, which were then uprooted.

Once more the sickening destruction of cinchona plantations was to take place, but the quinine industry claimed to be helpless. It was saddled with a continuously increasing surplus of the drug in spite of the fact that in 1924 the Kina Bureau had started regular propaganda, offering quinine at low prices to missions and governments for anti-malarial campaigns. There was, however, one obvious flaw in this propaganda, for sulphate of quinine from the Java bark, no matter how cheap, would be prohibitive in the great malarial areas. This was due to no frenzied urge for profit on the part of the manufacturers but, sulphate of quinine being already an expensive product, the industry had not been compelled by competition to improve its methods of manufacture and cultivation in order to obtain a cheaper product. As an example of this, while the Kina Bureau maintained that the drug could not be extracted at a profit from a bark yielding less than four per cent of quinine, the American Quinine Corporation in New York succeeded in doing it from bark yielding half, or less, that amount. The moral then was that those really concerned with the problem of malaria, which is the problem of destitute populations, should have developed their own sources of poor man's quinine while letting the Kina Bureau hold its own in the market for rich man's quinine.

But here is where the worst accusation against the Kina Bureau comes in: that by means not always quite ethical it made impossible and choked at birth any attempt to produce a source of cheap quinine, whether totaquine of one kind or another or possible synthetics. The Kina Bureau, which was not a philanthropic institution and never pretended to be one, was concerned with safeguarding the interests of the quinine industry and therefore could not relish the development of a cheaper competing product. Yet to assume that it actually stopped the whole world from developing such a product seems rather farfetched for, if true, either the Kina Bureau was endowed with diabolical powers or the rest of the world was unbelievably stupid.

The truth of the matter was that the world, besides being very hardhearted, was unbelievably shortsighted. To develop a source of quinine was no easy task, as exemplified by the Kina Bureau itself. The supremacy attained by the Dutch manufacturers over the quinine industry was the result of the successful adaptation of the ledgeriana in Java, which in its turn had been the result of a long and very expensive botanical experiment. Although, with the knowledge acquired, cinchona cultivation had become fairly simplified, cheap quinine could hardly attract private capital since, besides long-term returns and the problems of labor and location involved, it aimed at the most uncertain of markets. The wonder is that governments should also have been indifferent to the idea; but even

in the twentieth century it is still questionable whether statesmen do not consider disease an unavoidable act of God.

It was then by virtue of the many handicaps attending the
production of cheap quinine that the Kina Bureau held an
impregnable position. And those who fought it were really
waging war against the prevailing inertia. The British tem-
porized by having their only quinine factory supplied with
bark from British-owned plantations in Java. This course was
followed later on by Italy and had also been the policy of the
Japanese. Hoshi Seiyaku Company, Japanese manufacturers
of quinine, obtained bark from the large Japanese-owned
Sadareke plantation and from South America when it was
available. But Sadareke supplied only part of the bark and
Hoshi had to depend for the rest of it on the Kina Bureau.
And so Hoshi, who wanted to become independent of the
Bureau, set about to destroy it. Beginning as early as 1918,
agents and salesmen of Hoshi appeared as if by magic everywhere, offering sulphate of quinine below price and praising
the infinite wisdom of those who owned their own sources of
quinine. And to set an example, in 1918 a private Japanese
citizen, deputizing for Hoshi, bought a mountain tract in
Peru for the development of cinchona plantations.

In 1920 the Hoshi factory was destroyed by fire but it
joined with Kyodo Pharmaceutical Company and continued
to fight the Kina Bureau so successfully that, in 1922, as recorded in the *Chemist and Druggist*, a member of the Bureau
went in person to Java to persuade the Sadareke plantation to
join the Bureau, "since this is the only large plantation remaining outside the Agreement, and supplying bark to the Japanese
concern, which has now become a serious competitor of the
Kina Bureau in the international trade." Sadareke, however,

remained firm and eventually the Kina Bureau threatened retaliation against Hoshi for selling quinine below price by curtailing shipments of bark to Tokyo. Hoshi, through its agent in New York, William Hosken Inc., represented to the Department of Justice that by restraining trade the Kina Bureau was under purview of the Sherman Act. In 1927 the Department of Justice decided to prosecute the Kina Bureau.

Meanwhile, after the Department of Commerce had been reorganized under Secretary Herbert Hoover in 1921, the chief of the Chemical Division of the Bureau of Foreign and Domestic Commerce, Mr. C. C. Concannon, with the support of the director of the Bureau, began an intensive campaign to create an independent source of quinine for the United States by interesting either private capital or government agencies in the cultivation of cinchona in Central and South America. Such a campaign had been waged before. As early as in 1864 the American Medical Association had considered the suitability of cinchona plantations in Haiti as proposed by Dr. D. J. Macgowan. In 1867 the project was again brought to the fore by the Medical Society of Wayne County, Michigan, which presented to the Association a paper by one of its members, Dr. J. M. Bigelow, who in forceful terms demanded the introduction of cinchona cultivation in the United States. A committee was appointed by the American Medical Association to deal with Congress on the subject. Congress was relentlessly "memorialized" for seven years but without success and the committee gave up the fight in 1875. The legislators had somehow failed to become interested in the cinchona tree in spite of the fact that at the time the decisive role played by quinine in the Civil War should have been vivid in everybody's mind.

In our time the Bureau of Foreign and Domestic Commerce

was no luckier than the old committee, although it persisted
for several years in emphasizing by means of an educational
campaign the strategic weakness of the United States in regard
to the supply of quinine, particularly in case of armed conflict.
Thus when the Department of Justice decided to prosecute
the Kina Bureau, the Bureau of Foreign and Domestic Commerce pointed out that there was but one way of fighting it:
namely, by establishing an independent source of quinine.
This, however, would take several years and the Department
of Justice wanted quick action. But action against whom?
Certainly not against the members of the Kina Bureau, who
were outside the jurisdiction of the United States. Neither
did it seem practical to bring action against the manufacturers
of quinine in the United States, which were associates of the
Kina Bureau, since this would only result in depriving them
of the bark to manufacture quinine, which then would have to
be bought in Holland from the very members of the Kina
Bureau. To the suggestion that the manufacturers could buy
their bark in South America they replied that the supply of
South American barks was irregular, of low quality, and in-
sufficient, the latter due to the fact that the Kina Bureau itself
was South America's best customer for bark.

In spite of all these drawbacks, late in 1927 action was taken
against the Kina Bureau by the federal courts on a criminal
charge of conspiracy to violate various anti-trust acts. Shortly
after, a conference was called by Colonel William Donovan,
who was in charge of the prosecution, to which were summoned some twenty-five representatives of the Dutch and
American interests. Among them was a young Mr. van Linge,
who could help but little, his only connection with quinine
being that his father was the director of the Kina Bureau, but

he was forced to be there since on his refusal to attend the gathering, while visiting the United States, he had been informed of the startling fact that he was a material witness and therefore subject to arrest and incarceration. So drastic an action against Mr. van Linge, Jr., had apparently been taken with the expectation that his father would come rushing to his rescue and thus place himself within jurisdiction of the United States courts. Mr. van Linge, Sr., however, fearing little for his son's safety in the hands of American justice, failed to appear on the shores of the New World, and thus missed the spectacle of America regretfully emerging from its glorious days of innocence.

In March 1928 the United States seized and impounded in the port of New York a shipment of some five tons of quinine sulphate which was still technically the property of the Kina Bureau.

Finally an agreement was reached in September 1928 as the result of innumerable conferences and a visit by Colonel Donovan to The Hague, whereby all parties were perpetually enjoined by a consent decree from any practices constituting a violation of the Sherman, Clayton, and Wilson acts. The Department of Justice thus scored a technical victory over the Kina Bureau that has been compared to that of King Pyrrhus over the Romans, which cost the victorious king endless effort while doing little harm to his enemies. United States court decrees against Dutch nationals outside the jurisdiction of the United States were of only theoretical value since they could not be enforced, and by controlling ninety per cent of the world's production of bark the Kina Bureau was in absolute command of the situation. Nevertheless, by entering the arena for commercial supremacy as the redresser of wrongs, the United States had won the trophy as the only sovereign nation ever to challenge the Kina Bureau.

One positive result from the general commotion seems to have been that Merck and Company of New York, the largest manufacturer of quinine in the United States and therefore the biggest customer for bark of the Kina Bureau in the country, early in 1930 made their first appropriation for an experimental cinchona plantation in Guatemala. Mr. Concannon of the Bureau of Foreign and Domestic Commerce continued his relentless campaign to provide the United States with an independent source of quinine, which bore no fruit other than a general study of cinchona cultivation by the Department of Agriculture and the establishment in Puerto Rico of a small experimental cinchona plantation. The agents and salesmen of Hoshi continued to sell quinine below price.

In 1930 the I. G. Farbenindustrie in Germany announced that a synthetic compound, actually a dye named atabrine, had been discovered for the treatment of malaria. Suddenly the whole problem of quinine was changed. The new synthetic was hailed as being as good if not better than quinine. Interest in the latter declined and even Hoshi stopped fighting the Kina Bureau. The efforts of the Association of Bark Producers in Java to curtail the production of bark became intensified. Because these efforts had been partly neutralized by small independent growers who sold indiscriminately at any price they could get and were expanding handsomely by improving their methods of cultivation or devising new ones, the Association requested the government's help in averting the impending cinchona crisis.

On March 1, 1934, the government of the Netherlands East Indies passed the Cinchona Export Ordinance and the Cinchona Planting Ordinance. All exports of bark were forbidden from March 1934 to January 1937 unless covered by an export license; a license was also required for the amount of bark to be manufactured into quinine within the Netherlands Indies. During the first year this restriction was put into effect the bark exported was less than half the usual amount. By the Cinchona Planting Ordinance the government also limited the cultivation of bark and forbade the exportation of planting material by its plantations.

Then, about 1936, the general enthusiasm for atabrine began to decline. The problem of its dosage was complex and differences of opinion arose among the medical authorities as to whether it was as good, better, or inferior to quinine; the subject became definitely controversial. In addition, atabrine was expensive, its production being exclusively controlled by the I. G. Farbenindustrie. The medical profession on the whole went back to quinine as the old familiar remedy, the peculiarities of which the physician had mastered. The agents and salesmen of Hoshi became active once more with secret offers of quinine below price, while spreading the "raise quinine" message. But in 1936 Hoshi received an unexpected blow: the Peruvian Government questioned the validity of Hoshi's title to the mountain tract bought in 1918 for the cultivation of cinchona and the land reverted to the government with the exception of some two hundred acres already under cultivation. With the Sadareke plantation in Java under the restrictions of the Cinchona Export Ordinance, Hoshi discreetly surrendered. In 1937 the Japanese Government sent a mission to Java to negotiate trade relations between the two countries; its objective unaccomplished, the mission was still there four years later when Japan attacked Pearl Harbor.

If the voluminous documentation concerning the Kina Bureau and its manifold ramifications were presented to a reader who had never heard the word "quinine," after a most tedious reading he would be thoroughly mystified as to what quinine was. He would undoubtedly have gathered that it was a commodity of primary importance but he would not know whether it was a gas for mechanized warfare, a chemical explosive, or a basic ingredient for industrial manufacture. That it was a medicinal drug would hardly occur to him, for in the whole controversy the voices of the physician and the public health official are strangely silent; and the word "malaria" is seldom mentioned. That malaria is credited with having ruined whole civilizations, with keeping entire nations economically destitute, with making uninhabitable some of the richest lands on earth, thus leaving idle great sources of wealth, and that it brings misery and despair to millions of human beings, he would never surmise.

For this hypothetical reader's intelligence, then, a story could be told whose origins are lost in the world of antiquity. The story concerns a fabulous character named Hercules, the son of Jupiter, who in atonement for great sins had to perform twelve superhuman labors. But Hercules, being likewise superhuman in strength, easily coped with monsters and horrors of all description. One labor, however, he could not perform and that was to kill a huge Hydra with nine heads, the middle one of which was immortal. This Hydra dwelt in the swamps, a monster of cruelty that time and again brought ruin and misery to the people living near the swampy lands. Hercules, fiercely swinging his club, knocked off the monster's heads one by one but two new heads appeared for each one he destroyed. He was about to give up in despair when one of his nephews,

Iolaus, came to his assistance and Hercules finally succeeded in cutting the Hydra's immortal head, placing it under a big stone, lest it should come to life again.

His predicament overcome, Hercules resumed his exploits unaided, until faced with the sixth labor, which necessitated the clearing of certain marshes of the man-eating birds which gathered about them. Again the mighty Hercules was helpless, for he could not reach the birds and could not see them until Athena, coming to his help, gave him some brazen cymbals, by the clashing of which he put the birds to flight, and then shot them down with his unerring arrows. The next six labors, superhuman as they were, Hercules performed alone.

According to this legend, then, not even Hercules, the son of Jupiter, could destroy alone the Hydra of the swamps nor clear the marshes of the invisible man-eating birds. For how long mankind knew so accurately the story of malaria and how to get rid of it no one has ever known: first kill the Hydra —free of disease the people in the marshy lands; and then kill the birds—destroy the murderous mosquito. It is perhaps the greatest riddle that mankind can be endowed with such profound wisdom while indulging in the most chaotic behavior. For centuries Hercules had been fighting the Hydra and getting nowhere. Hercules was the medical profession; like him, a sinner and of superhuman courage. What the physician has written about "fevers" since the days of Hippocrates would fill many libraries. How intensely the physician's mind has elaborated on the cause of fevers would fill the ether of the universe, if thought, as light, reflected itself in space. The number of physicians who have died of malaria or have become disabled by it would make an endless list. One by one the physician helplessly knocked off the heads of the Hydra until quinine was brought to him by a group of men who in un-interrupted succession valiantly helped him to carry on the fight. The physician then found the way to use the new rem-edy, discovered the cause of the disease and how it is propa-gated; he fought his battle so well that for several years now malaria has been no longer a medical problem but a purely social and economic one. The invisible man-eating birds must be destroyed, but that the physician cannot do without the cymbals of Athena.

To the physician's delight, the brazen cymbals were pre-sented to him in due time: Athena was the League of Nations. One of the first results of the Malaria Commission of the League of Nations, that took as its emblem the Hydra of the swamps, was the staggering revelation that the number of malarial patients in the world was six hundred and fifty mil-lions; that is over one third of the human race, and lately this figure has been increased to eight hundred millions, or nearly one half of the human race. Compared to this, the amount of quinine produced in the world was so insignificant as to be negligible, and in 1924 the Health Organization of the League began a series of inquiries to prepare for an international con-ference to discuss the production of quinine.

In June 1928 the Malaria Commission held a conference to consider the best way of attacking the world-wide problem of malaria. From several countries malariologists, officials of the Rockefeller Foundation, engineers, and public health workers attended the conference and resolved that the first indispensable step was "to treat the sick." In 1929 the Com-mission made a survey tour of India and concluded that in the rural areas the problem of malaria was unbelievably serious; in the railway companies alone, out of nearly eight hundred thousand employees, more than six hundred thousand cases of malaria a year were treated. The Commission made recommendations and asked for appropriations to organize the distribution of quinine. Recommendations and appropriations, however, were of little value if there was no quinine, for all the bark produced in India and Java combined would hardly take care of India alone.

In January 1931 the Health Organization sent a circular letter to all the malarial countries, requesting information concerning their respective needs of the drug. One hundred and eleven nations answered the call and from the information received such facts appeared as to render belief in humanitarian principles a delusion of the feeble-minded; the amount of quinine imported by China, where three hundred and fifty million people live in malarial areas, was hardly enough for the treatment of half a million cases. Under the auspices of the Malaria Commission, beginning in 1933, international congresses on malaria were held every year, and beginning in 1934, yearly courses on malaria were given in Rome, Paris, Hamburg, London, and Singapore, to be followed by field work in Italy, Spain, and Yugoslavia.

In May 1934 a resolution was adopted whereby the use of totaquine or the mixture of alkaloids was to be recommended since by "its efficacy—equal or only slightly less than that of quinine—facility of preparation and cost of price, its use would enable malaria treatment to be extended over a wider field." A report by Dr. W. F. Fletcher on totaquine was to be distributed to all malarial countries and the Malaria Commission requested that the Health Organization "assist Health Departments who wish to employ this remedy . . . and to hold itself at the disposal of any Institute which may desire to continue this research."

Meanwhile since 1924 the League had been fostering the cultivation of red cinchona for the production of totaquine and through its efforts attempts were made to revive the plantations in St. Helena, Reunion, Burma, French Indo-China, Madagascar, and the Belgian Congo, and new ones were started in Formosa, the French Cameroons, Uganda, Eritrea, and New Guinea. In 1939 the U.S.S.R., where a most effective anti-malarial campaign has been carried out since the early twenties by means of quinine distribution, began large-scale experimental plantations of red cinchona. The British, who already had started new plantations in Africa before 1914, considered beginning new ones in India. According to a survey of possible locations, in Ceylon, where once the red cinchona had grown "from the ancient Kingdom of Kandy to the confines of the principality of Uvah," Spruce's beautiful tree was found to be growing still as handsome as ever in the most unexpected locations. When in 1942 a bad epidemic of malaria broke out in Ceylon, these scattered trees might have been of some use to the native, who in times past had not hesitated "to help himself to a strip of bark from the nearest tree when occasion necessitates it," had he not forgotten what the exotic tree was for. These few trees, however, were of little help, for out of a population of five million there were a million and a half cases of malaria, very few of whom actually received any medical care, and this in a country that once had produced thirteen million pounds of bark in a single year.

From 1935 to 1936 extensive experiments on the use of atabrine and plasmochin, another much debated synthetic, were carried out under the auspices of the Health Organization in Algeria, Italy, Malaya, Rumania, and Russia. In 1937 a three-year plan of studies on malaria was drawn up by the

Commission and a definite agreement was made to hold an intergovernmental conference on the production of quinine. In May 1939, after examination of the preliminary work by the subcommittee on totaquine, it was decided that the international conference on anti-malarial drugs, to which nineteen nations had already agreed, was to be convened at the end of 1940.

We all know what happened in September 1939 and how in 1940 the world was plunged in a war not against malaria, from which nations would emerge healthier and stronger, but a war against its own incompetence from which nations emerged ruined and devastated beyond belief. The clashing of Athena's cymbals was drowned by the mighty roar of battle; the man-eating birds of the marshes that had been put to flight came down unmolested to resume their destructive task freer than ever. In May 1940 Germany invaded Holland and the Kina Bureau with all the bark in stock became German property. In March 1942 the Japanese occupied Java and took possession of its great cinchona plantations, where a hundred years ago had grown the first cinchona outside the American hemisphere. Hoshi Seiyaku Company could have all the bark it wanted without having to beg other countries for bits of land and without submitting to the demands of the Kina Bureau. Japan could have the quinine without which the conquest of China was like grasping a red-hot iron with bare hands. The United States was faced with sending its armies to two of the great malarial areas of the world: North Africa and the Pacific.

In 1931 Winthrop Chemical Company of New York had begun to experiment with the manufacture of atabrine, which in 1932 was commercially available to the public; but atabrine was still a controversial subject. If the great United States of America, that astonishes the world with the endless stream of its production, wanted quinine, it would have to go for it to the cordilleras of the Andes, where the cinchonas have grown wild from time immemorial, and the Americans of the twentieth century would have to follow the tracks made long ago by the mad Jussieu, the melancholy Mutis, the tragic Caldas— the ill-fated prophets who first warned the world to keep good custody over the fever bark tree and whose message was unheeded and like them quickly forgotten. Once more the Indian gods of the forest were going to watch the little men run up and down the mountains in search of the fever bark tree.

CHAPTER XIV

Bataan and Corregidor

*Give me four physicians and I will give you back
four companies.* MARSHAL LYAUTEY

In the fourth century B.C. the armies of Alexander the
Great which feared nothing and knew only victory were
halted, disrupted, and deprived of their leader by the "fevers."
Since then many armies have surrendered to the same enemy.
When an army goes down fighting for whatever reason, it
may be a tragic event and in tragedy there is always dignity;
but when it surrenders as a shivering, shaking, vomiting lot
of men who have to be carried on stretchers by the enemy it
is sad and pitiful. It was no accident of fate that the medical
problem of malaria was solved by two army physicians, because both Laveran and Ross knew that neither courage nor
discipline nor armaments was of any use when a soldier fell
victim to malaria, and they had seen the humiliation of it.

In the spring of 1862, at the cry "On to Richmond," the
Army of the Potomac under McClellan advanced to within
seven miles of the city, where it stopped to wait for reinforce-
ments which did not come. Left to its fate in the Chickahominy Valley, McClellan's army was attacked by malaria.
In July it had withdrawn to Malvern Hill and McClellan's
men had given malaria another new name: Chickahominy
fever. General Lee was able to resume the offensive. In the

Spanish-American War, for each soldier wounded four came back sick with malaria. In World War I the offensive of Salonika had to be postponed, for out of a hundred and twenty thousand soldiers a hundred thousand had malaria. In 1939 the Japanese campaign in South China, in Kwangsi Province, was a total failure because of malaria. If the fevers stopped only conquering armies, the event might not be greatly lamented; but the fevers also paralyze and destroy defending armies.

In 1942 some eighty thousand American and Filipino soldiers surrendered to the Japanese on Bataan and Corregidor; they too, like the soldiers of Alexander, had succumbed to the fevers. For how long they could have resisted the enemy at that stage of the war is problematic; but once they had become sick, their surrender was inevitable, for the soldiers of this army in 1942, like those of Alexander more than two thousand years ago, had no means of combating the fevers.

The Japanese took the Philippines, but this was no easy territory for heathen conquerors to hold.

At the doors of Asia, the Philippines (named after Philip II, King of Spain) were brought within Christendom by the Spanish arm which reached across two oceans and one continent. For generations the Filipinos have been Christians and therefore Occidentals in their culture. Manila was the only occidental capital in the Orient where an occidental language was spoken and whose aristocracy could compete advantageously with any group anywhere in the Western world as to charm, wit, learning, and elegance. Manila was a beautiful city. When Spain lost the Philippines it was the signal that the long ailing Spanish Empire had finally died.

When the Philippines passed to the United States a new empire was born. Wealthy and strong, the new empire, with the enterprising spirit of youth, gave to its new subjects what exhausted Spain had not been able to give for a long time: the new and expensive tools of progress. Works of sanitation, urbanization, and public health were soon started in the Philippines, roads were built, and schooling was expanded. When in 1942 the Japanese occupied the Islands they found not only a hostile but an alien environment as well. Against their pagan religion rose the militant Castilian believer, and against their ancestral system of hierarchical government stood the modern American of the twentieth century. And whatever oriental element perforce survives in the Filipinos was also to the detriment of the Japanese, for it aided the former to carry on their most uncanny guerrilla war, a pursuit which, if kept on long enough, will bring thorough demoralization to any army of occupation. The guerrilleros were very brave and tenacious and could stand great hardships, but malaria was after them and would have done away with them if they had not had quinine bark.

Perhaps the most imaginative of all writers and the greatest master at creating breathless suspense was the Frenchman Jules Verne. In one of his novels, called *The Mysterious Island*, he describes a scene of unsurpassed drama: a group of men wrecked on a deserted island, one of them dying of malaria, suddenly discover neatly placed on a stone, previously empty, a box of tablets of quinine. The fact that the Philippine guerrillas were constantly provided with quinine bark under the very eyes of the Japanese partakes somehow of the same eerie quality of the episode created by Jules Verne. One can easily imagine the guerrilleros finding the drug in hollow trees, among bushes, and under stones; and whoever put it there, at the risk of his life, is better forgotten. As in Verne's novel, however, there was nothing eerie concerning the origins of the drug, which came simply from the Philippine cinchona plantations in Mindanao.

When the Americans first took possession of the Philippines, one of the great problems was the development of agricultural lands. To cope with this, a young forester named Arthur F. Fischer, recently graduated from the Yale School of Forestry and a reserve officer in the Military Intelligence, was sent to the Philippines by the government. Forestry is an extraordinary science that accomplishes what the honored sorcerer in all civilizations attempted to do and pretended to have done. Thus forestry can bring the rains, affect climates, and maintain the flow of rivers. In certain areas and at certain altitudes where the mosquito thrives, malaria makes forestry impossible, for its magic works not by incantations but by means of human labor.

Arthur Fischer, who was made director of the Bureau of Forestry in the Philippines in 1917, found this out very shortly. He had control over sixty per cent of the total area of the Philippine Islands and this included vast extensions of fertile lands never exploited. Great possibilities lay ahead of him but he could not use them, for as soon as malaria-infected individuals entered the virgin forest the mosquito would immediately begin the delicate operation of carrying the parasite from one man to another; reinfection was constant and manual work out of the question. An anti-malarial campaign was instituted in the Philippines and, according to Fischer's own description:

As the virgin forest was utilized, agriculture production beyond mere subsistence grew, mining followed as did fisheries and many collateral little industries, baking, rice milling, tanning, soap making, weaving and, as money became plentiful, shops appeared, houses (as compared to bamboo and palm-thatched dwellings), electric illumination, and power production with all of its ramifications, for the average live town followed in the wake of greater prosperity.

Such gratifying results, however, required an initial investment of considerable importance, which of necessity limited the extent of the campaign. All the quinine distributed free was imported, at the average price of one dollar and twenty-five cents per treatment; since the same individual had to be treated several times because of the recurrent type of malaria and reinfection, it was a very expensive drug.

Arthur Fischer began to consider the possibility of cinchona plantations. When Herbert Hoover sent his determined telegram to the Philippines bidding them "raise quinine," the order became a war cry, not very effective at the beginning, for as is often the case those who should have heeded it had first to see their own dead. Thus it was not until 1921 when General Wood, governor general of the Philippines, saw a young ranger die of malaria for lack of quinine while on duty in some forsaken spot, that decisive action was taken. Out of his own contingent funds General Wood gave four thousand dollars with which the American consul in Java obtained a bottle of ledgeriana seeds.

Under the direction of Arthur Fischer the plantations were started at Baguio. At first the enterprise seemed doomed to failure, for it was badly handicapped by unfavorable location, insects, disease, and droughts, duly reinforced by yards and yards of red tape knotted up in ingenious loops. But neither the contrary forces of nature nor those of officialdom prevailed, and in 1927 the plantations were moved to Mindanao, where ledgerianas, red cinchonas, and a hybrid of the two grew and bloomed. In 1936 the first shipment of eight thousand kilos of bark from Mindanao reached Manila, where a small factory had been established for the manufacture of totaquine, which was produced at a cost of seventeen cents per treatment as compared to one dollar and twenty-five cents with sulphate of quinine. According to the last report on this worthy project, dated March 1941, an enlarged factory had been built in Manila with a daily capacity for two kilos and a half of totaquine.

When the Japanese attacked the Philippines, resistance in Manila being useless, it was declared an open city and the American and Filipino troops, from sixty to ninety thousand men, withdrew to Bataan and Corregidor on January 1, 1942. This first campaign of the Philippines will always be a sorrowful page in the history of the United States. The enemy was powerful and well prepared in those days, and among the many unfortunate things that happened in the hasty retreat, perhaps the worst was leaving in Manila whatever stock there was of totaquine. Arthur Fischer, now Colonel Fischer in the Intelligence Service, had hoped to take along the factory machinery, with the intention of transporting it to the plantation in Mindanao to continue manufacturing the drug for the troops; but that too was left behind.

On Bataan and Corregidor the eternal fevers once more took their toll of human suffering; according to approximate calculations, about eighty-five per cent of the men became sick of malaria. They had some atabrine but it helped little. This was the first time atabrine had been given to a large group without proper medical supervision and, as the problem of its dosage was still unsolved, it gave the men temporary toxic reactions, which in their run-down condition weakened them considerably. It is common knowledge how Colonel Fischer, himself ill with malaria, flew to Mindanao in a desperate attempt to make a crude extract of cinchona bark. He succeeded in having a considerable number of trees peeled and the bark was placed in oil tins to be flown to Bataan and Corregidor, but it never got there. Bataan and later Corregidor had meanwhile surrendered.

General MacArthur, like the generals of Charles V, like the undaunted Barbarossa and so many other great generals before him, faced the grievous necessity of having his men surrender as a shivering, vomiting lot who should have been carried on stretchers by the enemy but instead were led into the March of Death; and, like those other generals, he knew the mortifying sorrow of it. General MacArthur knew at first hand what malaria can do to an army; and if Marshal Lyautey had been willing to exchange four companies for four physicians, MacArthur might have given half of his forces for quinine.

The Philippines were lost and Colonel Fischer was still on Mindanao. General MacArthur sent three Flying Fortresses to rescue important personnel including Colonel Fischer. The first two were shot down but in the third, with Japanese planes following closely, Colonel Fischer, still very ill, made his famous escape, carrying with him a box of ledgeriana seeds from the Mindanao plantations—the descendants in straight line of those seeds that seventy-six years ago the Indian Manuel Mamani had picked from a unique patch of fifty trees in the highlands of Bolivia, and which were sent to England in a box sewed in a hide. Many men had risked and lost their lives for this box of seeds that now a Flying Fortress was to bring back home in the custody of a sick man who only by a miracle did not pay for the gesture with his life. But with the ledgeriana plantations in the hands of the enemy, the box of seeds was a priceless possession because the patch of trees from which they originated will never again be found in the highlands of Bolivia.

In April 1942, Colonel Fischer reached the United States with his box of seeds, which were flown immediately to the Glenn Dale nurseries of the Department of Agriculture in Maryland, where they germinated without great difficulty. After several weeks in the Walter Reed Hospital, Colonel Fischer, scarcely recovered, began to take the necessary steps for starting government-owned cinchona plantations in Central America. As in his younger days in the Philippines, he successfully disentangled himself from many a red-tape snare and finally a contract was signed between the government of Costa Rica and the government of the United States, whereby Costa Rica granted a concession of ten thousand acres of land; there toward the end of 1943 two million cinchona seedlings were planted.

The men who had run the cinchona plantation in the Philippines remained there and continue to run it. Evading Japanese vigilance daily, they managed to prepare pills of a crude ground bark that were shipped throughout the southern Philippines, where malaria was rampant; and in time these pills were found in hollow trees and among bushes by the guerrilleros who, luckier than the defenders of Bataan and Corregidor, made life very difficult for the Japanese invaders. And in the midst of the frightful events that so undeservedly punished the Philippines, a familiar figure was seen reconstructing a forgotten scene of the past, the figure of Jesuit father James E. Haggerty, who, in defiance of the enemy, was one of the main instruments in getting the anti-malarial drug to the people. Thus he carried on the task begun three hundred years ago by the Jesuit, John de Lugo, as he distributed among the destitute the Jesuits' powder his predecessors had brought for the first time to the Orient, many decades ago, as a regal gift for a feverish Chinese emperor.

There is not the slightest doubt that the Philippine guerrillas prepared the ground for the reconquest of the Islands and that without quinine their task would have been impossible. In November 1945 the President of the Philippines awarded to Colonel Fischer the Distinguished Service Star for "his exceptional foresight, technical skill and courageous determination in providing the Philippines with local sources of raw material of quinine. . . ." In the citation there is also well-deserved mention of "the skill, resourcefulness, loyalty and courage shown by the men who continued operation of the plantation and distributed the bark throughout Mindanao and the Visayas under most difficult conditions during the Japanese occupation, thereby saving thousands of lives of guerrillas and civilians" and thus "reflected outstandingly the inspiring leadership and unselfish devotion which Colonel Fischer has given to this highly important project."

The disaster of the Philippines brought home the first bitter realization that the country was at war with strong and well-prepared enemies. The task ahead was colossal and on looking back on those fateful days it seems unbelievable that everything had to be started from the beginning, from the making of uniforms to the building of battleships. The diversity and complexity of the problems to be solved might have brought utter confusion to the best minds of the nation if soberly considered. But it is the advantage of war over peace that in the former there is no time for sober judgment. Any proposal for controlling malaria among a given population of several millions will invariably meet with considerations of a so-called practical order which in the end might raise insuperable obstacles to such a venture. Yet if the United States was to win the war, malaria had to be quickly controlled among the millions in the armed forces that would go to malarial areas—the Pacific, North Africa, southern Italy—irrespective of "practical" considerations. Such considerations no doubt had a great deal to do with the fact that the United States found itself without quinine and that atabrine was still a controversial subject eleven years after its discovery. Thus when in 1942 a scientific Board for the Co-ordination of Malarial Studies was organized under the auspices of the National Research Council its first step was to decide the atabrine controversy.

In the event, however, that atabrine might prove to be unsatisfactory, the Foreign Economic Administration sent four United States missions to Ecuador, Colombia, Peru, and Bolivia to gather bark from the wild cinchona forests of the Andes. Life came again to the silent cordilleras, long-forgotten trails were opened anew, and donkeys were seen carrying loads of bark as in the days of the Jesuit missionaries. Again the Indians of the highlands could show their skill in detecting the cinchonas within the maze of the tropical forest, and English-speaking botanists, resuming the long-neglected work of their Spanish predecessors, made a brave attempt at unraveling the natural history of the fever bark tree.

Thousands upon thousands of cinchonas were found in the slopes of the cordilleras: the red, the yellow, the gray, the orange, divided and subdivided in an infinite number of varieties: with large leaves, small leaves, lance-shaped leaves, round leaves, corrugated leaves, smooth leaves, leaves in all shades of red, brown, green; with pink flowers, white flowers, lavender flowers, red flowers, as if the Creator, in self-amazement at having made this unique work of nature, could restrain His fantasy no longer and had to indulge in a symphony of variations of color, shape, and form on the same perfect theme. In their jargon the botanists spoke with Anglo-Saxon inflection of the cordifolia of Mutis, the officinalis of La Condamine, the scrobiculata of Humboldt, the ovata of Ruiz and Pavón, and the succirubra of Pavón (well known as the red cinchona), the calisaya of Weddell, and even the *Cinchona josephiana*, a shrub of the same species that a kind soul had modestly dedicated to the memory of Jussieu.

A long, sad story was evoked by the mention of these names in the mountains of the Andes. It was a story of failures and disappointments, wonderful because the men in it had all been intensely alive, men of faith with strong beliefs for which they fought without face-saving reservations, by subterfuge sometimes, but never by petty or even mediocre means. All of them had been great in their own peculiar ways: the admirable John Cardinal de Lugo, the clever Sir Robert Talbor, seller of secrets, the vain La Condamine, the mad Jussieu, the melancholy Mutis, the tragic Caldas, the unlucky Spruce, the intriguing Manuel, and led by the noble Count of Chinchón, the rich and powerful grandee who, representing in his person the might of the Spanish Empire, had wept for the sorrows of the Indians of Peru.

The Americans too paid their price for intruding into the abode of the Indian gods. Arthur Featherstonehaugh, one of the members of the mission to Ecuador, died of altitude sickness due to a weak heart, and his body had to be carried down the mountain in a stretcher, through impassable jungle paths and along narrow trails bordering precipitous slopes, under sheets of rain. Fevers, jungle sores, and clouds of insects pursued the Americans, whose clothes rotted in the dampness of the forest.[1] The United States missions returned at the end of 1944, after having shipped home some fifteen thousand tons of bark, and in November 1945 all agreements with the South American governments for the collection of bark were terminated.

The cordilleras of the Andes are silent again and very soon the tropical forest will cover the lonely trails. The Indians of the highlands are back making pottery and weaving baskets, the fever bark tree will continue to grow in the mountain slopes unmolested, the Indian gods can go back to their timeless slumber surrounded by the solitude of nature, and it may very well be that never again will their peace be disturbed. For while the Americans ran up and down the Andean mountains in search of the cinchonas, others at home were busy exploring the intricate forest of chemical formulae and biological phenomena.

From 1942 on, in commercial firms, in universities and scientific institutions, in the medical departments of the army and navy, in the United States Public Health Service, the most exhaustive research on the problem of malaria was carried out. The question of atabrine was immediately solved, the proper dosage was determined and, as stated by the Board of Co-ordination of Malarial Studies, it proved to be even superior to quinine. The search for other synthetic anti-malarials, however, was continued, and of fourteen thousand compounds

[1]Froelich Rainey, "Quinine Hunters in Ecuador," *National Geographic Magazine*, March 1946.

that were studied one, called SN 7618, appears to be still better than atabrine; it seems to be more effective in smaller doses and it does not cause the yellowish pigmentation of the skin that atabrine causes on occasions, which, though harmless, is obviously not pleasant for the patient; neither does it cause the intestinal upsets that atabrine is apt to cause in certain cases.

Another line of research has been in the direction of finding a cure for the recurrent type of malaria, where medication with atabrine or quinine will put a stop to the disease though for several years, about three as a rule, the patient is apt to come down with occasional attacks of fever. Progress in this direction seems to be very encouraging. In fact there is already a compound named plasmochin—like atabrine, a product of the I. G. Farbenindustrie—which, according to the work of British investigators several years ago, was found to cure recurrent malaria when administered after treatment with quinine. However, plasmochin is not sufficiently harmless for its use to be recommended and other compounds of similar structure that may have the same curative effects without the danger of possible toxicity are being studied.

This very sketchy account of the work done on malaria during the war can give no idea of the skill, ability, and tireless effort of the men who carried it out and who, in laboratories and hospitals, won the major battle of the war as shown by the staggering statistics on malaria. The number of hospital admissions for malaria in the army and navy was 530,940, without including the first campaign of the Philippines where about eighty-five per cent of the troops had malaria, which would bring the total figure to about 600,000. This count is by hospital admissions, which of course means that in many instances the same man was admitted several times for recurrence and reinfection. But since, on the other hand, the cases that did not go to hospital are not included in these statistics, it can be assumed that 600,000 would be the approximate total number of cases of malaria, although this may be a very conservative estimate. From a military point of view, however, each admission meant a man out of action. To emphasize the relative importance of malaria incidence in the armed forces, it will suffice to say that it was over half the total number of casualties, which, as published in September 1945, was 1,070,-452. The total number of wounded was put at 651,261—that is, only 51,261 more than the total number of malarial patients, which was well over twice the total number of dead, over five times the total number of prisoners, and more than fifteen times the number of missing. In 1943 fifteen per cent of the army overseas had malaria, which was equivalent to four per cent of the total army.

If it had not been possible to treat these 600,000, this would have been the greatest disaster of the war. Avoidance of the disaster was due to the great contribution of the symbolic four physicians Marshal Lyautey longed for in malaria-ridden French North Africa, the men of science who, spectacularly on occasions but as a rule unobtrusively, many a time held in their hands the decisive factor in the fortunes of war. The 600,000 men who fell prey to the fevers received proper medical attention. With few exceptions, after a short illness they all could go back to serve their country in the hour of need. Some died a tragic death no doubt but not a pitiful one, shivering with fever in a prisoners' camp, as was the fate of many of the men who surrendered on Bataan and Corregidor. Some of them are still suffering from occasional recurring attacks of fever which in time will disappear and for which a cure is eagerly sought. That these recurrences should take place is regrettable; but if the men knew how much worse their condition might have been if there had been no drug against malaria they would be thankful at having escaped far worse discomforts. What their condition might have been many do know, because they have seen it in China, in India, in Guadalcanal, in the Philippines, and in so many other places where men, women, and children have stared helplessly at them with sunken faces, swollen bellies, and emaciated bodies—eternal victims of the eternal fevers.

In looking toward the future, however, it will be well to remember that this country had no plantation sources of quinine, that atabrine, which was not manufactured here until Germany entered the war, was still a controversial subject when the United States was attacked by Japan, that had it proved to be inadequate the wild cinchona forests of South America were the only source of quinine left to the Allies, and that no effort has ever been made in the past to preserve and increase these forests, which might have been extinct if predictions made repeatedly during the past hundred years had been fulfilled. England may have contributed some totaquine from the plantations in British India, but she could ill afford to do this, taking into consideration the fact that her railways alone have 600,000 cases of malaria each year among their employees and that, to top all misfortunes, in 1942 an epidemic of malaria broke out in India of such severity that thousands of young cinchonas had to be felled and stripped of their bark long before harvest time. In short, for a brief but paralyzing moment it was necessary to face the possibility of not being able to control malaria in the armed forces, at least for some time to come, while Japan would have had command of the Pacific, and the landing in North Africa would have been impossible. The strange events that led to this situation make up the story in this book which, as has been said at the beginning, is not a new tale because man, who is a monotonous animal, works against his salvation every time opportunity affords itself.

CHAPTER XV

Of Fevers

In 1930 warning was given that in Natal, the capital of the state of Rio Grande do Norte in Brazil, the mosquito *Anopheles gambiae* had been found. The gambiae, which makes of Africa the grave of the white man and was apparently brought to Brazil in a fast mail boat from Dakar, is the most dangerous carrier of malaria because it feeds almost exclusively on man, whom it constantly pursues by breeding as near as possible to his dwelling. This warning was ignored and in 1938, 100,000 people were sick in the areas adjacent to Natal; 20,000 died. In 1939 there were 185,000 cases of malaria. The health officials who visited the stricken area sent the following reports:

The situation grows worse from day to day. . . . The chief local authority . . . places the loss on the cotton crop at 60 per cent, the reduction in the extraction of carnauba wax at 80 per cent, with a similar falling off in the salt production. . . . The trip was a truly depressing experience since we saw entire families along the road, blocking the passage of the car as they begged for medicine. . . . It would take too long to narrate here all the sad details of the trip. . . . It took will power to continue the program of investigation instead of giving way to the insistence of the ragged and hungry multitude which pleaded for mercy at the side of the road. . . . The mortality has been terrific. . . . A new cemetery opened in Sacramento. . . . Hour by hour, day by day, the number of the sick increased. . . . The stock of medicines rapidly gave out. . . .[1]

[1]Fred L. Soper and D. Bruce Wilson, *Anopheles Gambiae in Brazil*. The Rockefeller Foundation, New York, 1943. Reprinted by permission.

Such scenes had not been recorded in the Western world since the great pandemics of the Black Death. The Brazilian Government, with help from the Rockefeller Foundation, succeeded in eradicating the *Anopheles gambiae* from the American continent. It was one of the most thorough and well-conducted sanitation campaigns ever achieved and one of the most rewarding as well. Had the gambiae spread in the American hemisphere, it would have been the greatest disaster in American history and might have changed the course of that history as had already been the case in a section of Brazil where entire villages were abandoned and lands were left to waste, as in Greece, Rome, and so many other places all over the world. Malaria is not always the chronic endemic disease that seeps away the life of its victims in a slow though fatal process of destruction. Malaria can be fulminant like the plague; and the epidemic in Brazil is the fourth already recorded within the last seventy years.

This epidemic of malaria in Brazil raises a question long debated by historians. Is malaria the cause of the economic and political decay of the countries it has invaded or was the invasion of malaria only possible after political and economic decadence had set in? If malaria, when first attacking a new region, took the epidemic form it took in Brazil, we know the answer to this question. How many of these epidemics there have been in history it is impossible to know because they could easily pass unidentified. Natal, in Brazil, is a malarial country, and yet when the epidemic brought about by the new carrier first began the local physicians thought they were dealing with a new disease, so different is acute epidemic malaria from the chronic endemic type.

An epidemic like the one in Brazil, at a time when the cause of the disease was unknown and there was no medication for it, would ruin any nation and there would be no possible recovery because malaria, unlike the Black Death and the other great pandemics, stayed forever once it came. In a refinement of cruelty, nature would allow the victims of malaria to develop resistance to the disease, not enough to be cured and therefore immune to further attacks, as in the case of the Black Death, but only enough to modify the acute epidemic form into the chronic endemic disease common today which, as shown by the experience in Natal, is totally different in appearance from the former. It fails to protect the patient from other varieties of the malarial parasite and from new carriers, due to the complete absence of cross immunity. It could be said that if malaria did not undergo this modification, from the acute into the chronic form, it might have succeeded in wiping out the whole of the human race.

It is an almost infallible rule that anyone who gets more or less involved in the subject of malaria reaches the conclusion that it is the root of all the world's evils and therefore that its eradication would be the solution to all of them; and the author of this book is no exception to the rule. To explain the world's incredible confusion on the basis of one single cause is indeed to simplify things to an extent quite inadmissible by the student of human behavior and the observer of natural phenomena. Man, says the former, is exceedingly complex in his motivations and reactions, which are strongly conditioned by his culture and general environment. According to the latter, culture and environment are in their turn determined by geographical conditions, the most important being climate and natural sources of production. Both assertions seem to be undeniable. Yet in spite of his complexities and contradictions, man is universally subservient to an elementary force called the biological urge to survive. No matter how terrible his plight may be, he will live in the most unnatural conditions: in prison, in slavery, in sorrow, in sickness, in hunger, and in shame. Suicide is the generally recognized deviation and never before in the Western world have we had so clear and painful an instance of it as we have today.

If the biological urge to survive is accepted as true, then it follows that man will strive above all to preserve his life, from which strife stems the force of material progress; and his failures to use this force constructively is merely the result of man's moral and intellectual limitations. Yet to ascertain the difference in degree attained by material progress in malarial and non-malarial areas takes only a glance at a geographical-distribution map of this disease. So large is the area where malaria prevails that it includes all cultures, all religions, all races, all climates, poor lands and lands of in-finite wealth, and in all of them, regardless of culture, religion, race, and climate, there are economic chaos, political confu-sion, superstitious beliefs, misery, and starvation. Can it be that the man in China, in India, or in Africa is deprived of the biological urge to survive? Can it be that he is content to die young and see his children dead? Perhaps he is. We in the occidental world know very little of the man in China, in India, or in Africa. Or can it be that, physically incapacitated for hundreds of years by a crippling disease, he has found refuge in fatalistic philosophies that make the unavoidable death of the young acceptable and perhaps even desirable?

Unfortunately there is not experimental evidence one way or the other, because the problem of malaria has never been approached. The India experiment, the campaign in Italy, the first nation to pass legislative measures against malaria, and the anti-malarial campaign in the Philippines gave us only a glimpse of what can be accomplished by eradicating this disease because in the first place, in India due to economic rivalries, and in Italy and the Philippines due to the war, the original plans never reached full completion.

The moment has come now when the experiment may be tried, when in fact it has to be tried, because the existence of malaria in our present culture is a dangerous anachronism. Again an effort will be made to find solutions to the manifold problems that face the world; new boundaries will be drawn, new international treaties will be signed, new trade agreements will be devised, the problems of currencies, production, labor, demand, transportation, and distribution will be carefully studied. Whatever solutions are found, they will have to be of international scope and this will be impossible as long as millions of people all over the world are unable to provide for themselves, and therefore to solve properly their own economic problems, by being physically incapacitated. The eradication of malaria will be a long and arduous experiment requiring above all international co-operation; it will serve a moral as well as material end, for never before has mankind been more in need of common objectives. If those (including the author) who believe malaria to be the root of all evils are right, it will be a magnificent experiment. Rich lands will no more be wasted and where the jungle now grows new cities will spring up; natural resources will no longer lie idle, for goods will have to be supplied to the new cities around the rich lands; empty regions will be developed as outlets for the overcrowded ones; industrial improvements will be feared no more because what the world produces today, compared to what the world could consume (if the whole world *could* consume), is a fraction of a fraction.

Material progress, whether for good or evil, is an elementary force that cannot be stopped but can at best be harnessed; the eight hundred million who suffer from malaria will not suffer forever, and the changes that should come in an orderly and intelligent fashion may come through untold violence and by the long and painful road of incompetence and inefficiency.

Until the war made malaria once more the *great military problem*, the production of anti-malarial drugs was absolutely inadequate, as shown in the case of atabrine. In 1932 atabrine sold at sixty-six dollars and sixty-six cents per thousand tablets; with the war, which increased the demand from five million tablets a year to three billion tablets in 1944, the price for the government went down to three dollars per thousand tablets— that is, a reduction of sixty-three dollars and sixty-six cents. Thus, whereas in 1932 a treatment with atabrine cost about one dollar, it now costs exactly four and a half cents at the price sold to the government and six cents at the regular wholesale price of four dollars per thousand tablets. Such a low price is probably dependent on a large-scale demand, which could easily be maintained if the problem of malaria were no more than touched, for three billion tablets would scarcely take care of one eighth of the total population living in malarial areas.

From the progress made in the synthetic anti-malarials[2] during the war it will thus appear that quinine is fighting its final battle. The chemical synthesis of quinine by R. B. Woodward

[2]D.D.T. is exceedingly successful in destroying the mosquito but it can only be used in limited areas because of the fact that it also destroys a large number of other insects of a beneficial nature.

and W. E. Doering of Harvard University, which was so enthusiastically and deservedly greeted, was the end of a long search begun by Pasteur a hundred years ago. It was a long search but a very profitable one, for it was through the attempt to synthetize quinine that aniline purple, the first coal dye, was discovered by Perkin and a whole new industry was born. And it was as a result of working on the chemical structure of quinine that Land devised a cheap transparent plastic that could polarize light; another new industry developed, which in time sponsored the synthesis of quinine, fearing, with good reason, that the supply of cinchona bark from the Far East might be cut off. Synthetic quinine, however, is so far too expensive a process for commercial purposes.

As for atabrine, although it has proved invaluable for military purposes, the problem of its distribution to large populations for self-medication without medical supervision is still to be solved. As stated by Commander Hudson of the United States Navy:

There is one field in which quinine may retain pre-eminence; this is among the primitive malaria-ridden peoples of the tropics. It takes intelligence and medical supervision to use atabrine properly, and the goal of atabrine therapy is eventual eradication of the disease. Among primitive peoples suffering from hyperendemic chronic malaria without benefit of medical service, the object of treatment is mere relief from the temporary exacerbations of the disease. This is the proper place for the inexpensive but effective mixture of cinchona alkaloids known as totaquine. The prompt relief secured by small doses of quinine and the wide margin of quinine safety in unintelligent hands, may give it a considerable field for a long time to come.[3]

[3]E. H. Hudson, "Quinine and Atabrine," *United States Naval Medical Bulletin*, July 1945, Vol. 45, No. 1. Reprinted by permission.

Moreover, there is also a minority of people who are susceptible to intoxication by synthetic drugs, and so far quinine hydrochloride given by intravenous injection is the fastest-acting drug when emergency treatment is required in case of acute malignant malaria, particularly with cerebral involvement.

It would thus seem that quinine still has its uses. There is also the question of production and distribution. If the problem of malaria is ever going to be tackled on a world-wide basis, local production of anti-malarials would be necessary and the manufacture of synthetics would be completely out of the question in the malarial areas where industry is nonexistent but where there is as a rule a strong agricultural tradition. Plantations of the easy-growing red cinchona for the production of totaquine may be the solution in such cases, following the pattern of the government plantations in British India and the Philippines. Thus Colonel Fischer's main purpose when he began the United States Government plantations in Costa Rica was to make them a center from which planting material would be distributed for local production of totaquine in the Western Hemisphere, wherever geographical conditions would allow it.

There is also the supply of wild bark from South America which, though considerable, was neglected in favor of the Java barks. Consideration is being given to the possibility of developing on the Andean slopes natural orchards of cinchonas from which totaquine could be manufactured locally in the South American countries. In this connection the field method for the extraction of quinine devised by Major Robert L. Kaye in Fort Belvoir, Virginia, would be of excellent use. As a result of the war totaquine was manufactured in this hemisphere for the first time by S. B. Penick and Company of New York, from South American barks that proved to be excellent for the purpose.

As for sulphate of quinine, there is no information regarding its main source, the ledgeriana barks from Java, due to the political situation in the Dutch East Indies, although it would seem that the plantations have been kept in good order. At any rate, Merck and Company of New York intend to continue and expand their plantations in Guatemala for the manufacture of both sulphate of quinine and totaquine.

The problem, thus briefly discussed, of the ways and means of dealing with the problem of malaria will be the concern of the experts, who will have to make the final decision as to the best available solution. If in the near future quinine happens to be definitely displaced by the synthetics, it will always remain a unique landmark in the history of medicine. And when in the Andes the fertile valleys flourish and new cities are built above them on the slopes of the cordilleras, there will not be wanting some sedate person who, unmindful of the progress of his day, will peer curiously into the past and will tell the children of future American generations about that beautiful and useless tree in their back yard which was once the most important plant in the whole kingdom of nature and which some Spanish conquistadors in ages long past had named the fever bark tree.

Bibliography

Throughout the book several main sources of information have been used: Castiglioni, A., *Historia de la Medicina*, Barcelona, 1941; Sprengel, K., *Histoire de la médicine*, Paris, 1815; Haller, A. V., *Bibliotheca Medicinae Practica*, Bernal, 1779; Creighton, C., *A History of Epidemics in Britain*, Cambridge, 1891–94; Hirsch, A., *Handbook of Geographical and Historical Pathology*, London, 1883–86; *The Mythology of All Races*, Boston, 1916–32; various dictionaries such as Moreri, L., *Le Grand Dictionnaire historique*, Amsterdam, 1702; Moreri and Bayle, *General Dictionary*, 1734–41; Hooper, R., *Lexicon Medicum; or Medical Dictionary*, London, 1831; *Biographical Dictionary*, London, 1761; *Dictionary of National Biography*, *Encyclopaedia Britannica*, and *Enciclopedia Espasa Calpe*.

CHAPTER I

The main sources for the historical sketch on malaria have been: Daremberg, C., *Histoire des sciences médicales*, Paris, 1870; *Œuvres choisies d'Hippocrates*, Paris, 1855, by the same author; Jones, W. H. S., *Hippocrates*, New York, 1923; Celli, A., *The History of Malaria in the Roman Campagna*, London, 1933; and Hoops, A. L., "History of Malaria," *Malayan Medical Journal*, 1933–35, Vols. 8–10. For the description of the role played by malaria in Greece the main source has been Jones, W. H. S., *Malaria and Greek History*, Manchester, 1909. The biographical data on Alexander are from the life of Alexander in Plutarch's *Lives* and the data concerning his illness and death are from Ber-

BIBLIOGRAPHY

tolotti, M., *"Alessandro Magno," La Critica Medica nella Historia*, Turin, 1932, where the author establishes the striking parallel of Alexander's death with that of Lord Byron described in Chapter VIII.

CHAPTER II

The biographical data on the Count of Chinchón are from his own memoir, *Memorias de los Virreyes del Perú* . . . , Lima, 1899; from Suardo, J. A., *Diario de Lima (1629–34)*, Lima, 1935; and from Paz Soldan, C. E., *Las Tercianas del Conde de Chinchón*, Lima, 1938. The data about the medicinal herbs used by the American Indian are mainly from Pardal, R., *Medicina Aborigene Americana*, Buenos Aires, 1938. As to the conclusion that the Count of Chinchón was most likely the person who first brought the bark to Europe, it is based on Haggis, Λ. W., "Fundamental Errors in the Early History of Cinchona," *Bulletin of the History of Medicine*, 1941, Vol. 10, No. 3, and Vol. 10, No. 4.

CHAPTER III

The biographical data on John Cardinal de Lugo are from: Rompel, J. S. I., *"Kardinal de Lugo als Mäzen der Chinarinde, 1. Aus dem Leben das Kardinal,"* *75 Jahre Stella Matutina Festschrift*, Vol. I., Feldkirch (Selbstverlag Stella Matutina), 1931; and Nieremberg, J. E., *Varones Ilustres de la Compañía de Jesús*, Vol. 9, Bilbao, 1887–92. The historical background of the time is mostly from Ogg, D., *Europe in the Seventeenth Century*, London, 1925. The titles of the books concerning the quinine controversy mentioned in the chapter with English titles translated from the original Latin are the following: Chifletius, J. J., *Pulvis Febrifugus Orbis Americani Ventilatus*, Antwerp, 1653; Conygius, A., *Pulvis Peruvianus Vindicatus de Ventilatore Ejusdemque Suspecta Defensio*, Rome, 1655; Plempius, V. F., *Antimus Conygius, Peruviani Pueveris Febrifugi Defensor, Repulsus a Melippo Protimo Belga,*

1665. The latter was available only in a handwritten copy from the Army Medical Library, which was read to the author by Professor Arturo Castiglioni. The biographical data on V. F. Plempius come mostly from Ball, J. M., *Mag. Med.*, Vol 11, Atlanta, 1897; and Haan, *"Notice sur la vie et les ouvrages de V. F. Plemp,"* *Annuaire de l'université catholique de Louvain*, Louvain, 1845.

CHAPTER IV

The data relating to the introduction of quinine in England are mainly from Baker, Sir George, "Observations on the Late Intermittent Fevers to Which Is Added a Short History of the Peruvian Bark," *Medical Tracts*, London, 1818. Sir George Baker's paper was also used for the preceding chapter and is one of the main sources for Chapter V. Concerning Sydenham's opinion of the bark, his own statement on the drug in Sydenham, T., *Methodus Curandi Febres*, Amsterdam, 1666, was carefully translated from the original Latin with the help of Professor George A. Kubler.

CHAPTER V

Besides Sir George Baker's paper, the main sources are the *Lettres de Madame de Sévigné*, collected and annotated by M. Monmerque . . . Paris 1862–68; Blegny, N. de, *Le Remède anglois pour le guérison des fièvres*, Paris, 1682; Monginot, François de, *De la guérison des fièvres par le quinquina*, Paris, 1680; and Talbor, R., *A Rational Account of the Cause and Cure of Agues*, London, 1672. There is only one known copy of the latter in the United States, which is in the possession of Dr. George Dock, who very kindly lent it to the Historical Library of the Yale School of Medicine for the author's use. Several contemporary and later accounts were consulted for the historical background and the events connected with the Popish Plot; a very vivid reconstruction of the Plot that was exceedingly helpful is Carr, John Dickson, *The Murder of Sir Edmund Godfrey*, New York, 1936. As for the hypothesis that Sir Robert Talbor was sent to France by Charles II to save him from the instigators of the Popish Plot, it is the author's own conclusion in view of the coincidences between dates and events.

CHAPTER VI

One of the main sources is Harvey, G., *The Conclave of Physicians*, London, 1685. Concerning La Condamine's Expedition and the biographical data on La Condamine, the sources are: Le Sueur, A., *La Condamine d'après ses papiers inédits*, Paris, 1911; La Condamine, C. M. de, *Journal du voyage fait par ordre du roi . . .* , Paris, 1751; and La Condamine, C. M. de, *"Sur l'arbre du quinquina,"* *Mémoires de l'Académie des Sciences*, Paris, 1738. An effort has been made to reconstruct the biographical sketch of Joseph de Jussieu from the scanty data found about him in La Condamine's *Journal;* Ulloa, A. de, and Jorge, Juan, *Relación Histórica del Viage a la América Meridional . . .* Madrid, 1748; and Jussieu, J. de, *Description de l'arbre à quinquina, mémoire inédit de . . .* , Paris, 1936.

CHAPTER VII

The biographical data on José Celestino Mutis is almost exclusively from Gredilla y Gauna, A. F., *Biografía de José Celestino Mutis . . .* , Madrid, 1911. Concerning the Botanical Institute and the biographical data on Francisco José de Caldas, one of the main sources is Vezga, F., *La Expedición Botánica*, Bogotá, 1936. As to the measures taken by the Spanish Government concerning the exploitation of the cinchonas the main source is Restrepo y Tirado, E., *"Apuntes sobre la quina,"* *Boletín de Historia y Antigüedades*, Bogotá, 1943, Vol. 30.

BIBLIOGRAPHY

CHAPTER VIII

As mentioned above, the data on Lord Byron's death come from Bertolotti's *"Alessandro Magno."* The facts concerning Dr. John Sappington are mainly from his own book, *The Theory and Treatment of Fevers*, Arrow Rock, Missouri, 1844; and from Ackerknecht, E. H., "Malaria in the Upper Mississippi Valley," Supplement to the *Bulletin of the History of Medicine*, Baltimore, 1945. Concerning the events of the Castelnau expedition, the main source is Castelnau, F., Comte de, *Expédition dans les parties centrales de l'Amérique du Sud . . .*, Paris, 1850–61. Concerning Weddell and the historical data on the exploitation of the *Cinchona calisaya* in Bolivia, the sources are, Weddell, H. A., *Histoire naturelle des quinquinas*, Paris, 1849; and *Voyage dans le nord de la Bolivie . . .*, London, 1853, by the same author. The biographical data on Delondre are from Delondre, A., and Bouchardat, A., *Quinologie*, Paris, 1854.

CHAPTER IX

The biographical data on Laveran are mostly from Phisalix, M., *Alphonse Laveran, sa vie, son œuvre*, Paris, 1923; and Sergent, E., and Perrot, E. and L., *La Découverte de Laveran*, Paris, 1929. On the discovery of the mosquito as the carrier of malaria, one of the main sources is Ross, Ronald, *Memoirs . . .*, London, 1923. The biographical data on Dr. A. F. A. King come from the *Dictionary of American Biography*, New York, 1943.

CHAPTER X

The historical data on the Aymara Indians are almost exclusively from McBride, G. M., *The Agrarian Indian Communities of Highland Bolivia*, New York, 1921. Concerning Hasskarl's expedition to South America and the early history of the cinchona plantations in British India and in Java, some of the main sources are, Markham, C. R., *Peruvian Bark*, London, 1880; and *Travels in Peru and India*, London, 1862, by the same author. The biographical data concerning Richard Spruce are from Markham's, *Peruvian Bark*, and Spruce, R., *Notes of a Botanist on the Amazon and Andes*, edited by A. R. Wallace, London, 1908.

CHAPTER XI

The story of Ledger and Manuel Mamani has been reconstructed almost exclusively from Ledger's letters to John E. Howard, published by the latter in his *Quinology of the East Indian Plantations*, London, 1876; and also from Howard, J. E., "Origin of the Calisaya Ledgeriana of Commerce," *Pharmaceutical Journal*, March 13, 1880.

CHAPTER XII

Besides Markham's *Peruvian Bark* and Howard's *Quinology of the East Indian Plantations*, the main sources are the *Parliamentary Blue Books* (East India Cinchona) containing the official correspondence on cinchona cultivation, extracts of which are quoted both in this chapter and in Chapter X.

CHAPTER XIII

Factual information concerning the early events that led to the formation of the Kina Bureau comes from Cloetta, A., *Le Problème économique et social de la quinine* . . . (Thesis), Basel, 1928. Other sources are Kerbosch, A., "Cinchona Culture in Java," in *Proceedings of the Celebration of the Three Hundredth Anniversary of the First Recognized Use of Cinchona*, St. Louis, Mis-

BIBLIOGRAPHY

souri, 1931; "The World's Cinchona Bark Industry," *Great Britain Imperial Institute Bulletin*, Vol. 37, London, 1939, also used in Chapter X concerning the various attempts made in different parts of the world to cultivate the cinchona; and all throughout the chapter use has been made of newspapers, journals, and official records, including the reports of the Malaria Commission of the League of Nations.

CHAPTER XIV

The main sources are also newspapers, journals, and official records, recent scientific publications on malaria, and personal recollections of the campaign in the Pacific. The facts concerning the role played by quinine during the Civil War in the United States, in this chapter and in Chapter XIII, come from Churchman, J. W., "The Use of Quinine During the Civil War," *Johns Hopkins Hospital Bulletin*, Vol. 17, No. 183, Baltimore, 1906.

CHAPTER XV

The information concerning the production of atabrine was kindly provided by the Winthrop Chemical Company of New York.

Index

INDEX

Board of Co-ordination of Malarial Studies, 243, 245

Boerhaave, Hermann, 118, 130

Bogotá, 18, 111–13, 116–18, 120, 121, 123, 124, 126, 128–33

Bolivia, 143–46, 148–50, 169, 172, 173, 176, 184, 189–95, 207, 214, 240, 241, 243

Bonpland, Aimé Jacques Alexandre, 128, 129

Botanical Institute of Madrid, 134

Botanical Institute of the New Kingdom of Granada, 109–34

Botanist, work of the, 99, 103, 111, 121, 177, 195

Bouguer, Pierre, 99, 100–02

Brazil, 251

British Guiana, 138

Broughton, John, 186, 201

Buenos Aires, 18

Burma (British), 188, 207, 231

Byron, George Gordon, Lord, 136, 137, 138

Calancha, Father (Augustinian monk), 24, 27, 29

Caldas, de, Francisco José, 124, 127–34, 233, 244

Callao, 175

Cambridge University, 66, 81, 83

Cape Verde Islands, 188, 207

Caravaya (forest), Peru-Bolivia, 173, 174, 178, 184, 189–90

Cascarillero (bark collector), 144, 145, 173, 194

Castelnau, Francis de la Porte, Count of, 146, 148, 180

Caventou, Joseph Bienaimé, 142, 143, 149, 184

Celli, Italian scientist, 162

Central America, 222, 241

Ceylon, 182–83, 207, 231; malaria epidemic (1942), 231

Charles II of England, 56, 57, 72, 75, 84, 87, 88, 90

Chauliac, de, Guy, 12

Chemist, work of the, 127, 142

Chemist and Druggist, 221

Chiflet, Joan Jacob, 44–46, 51–52, 60

Chimborazo, volcano, 180, 181

China, malaria, 138, 248; quinine imports, 230

Chinchón, Francisca, Countess of, 23, 30, 31, 103

Chinchón, Luis Geronimo Fernandez de Cabrera Bobadilla Cerda y Mendoza, Count of, 20–24, 28–32, 244

Cinchona (tree), 115–16, 121, 126, 128, 143, 149, 151, 172, 173, 175, 176, 177, 200, 212, 214, 233, 243, 245, 248; bark gathering, 105, 115, 144, 145; botanical features unknown, 145; cultivation, 105, 122, 144, 219, 220; geographical distribution, 116, 119, 120, 127, 129, 132, 151; growth, 127; Java, 151; named, 31; South America, 187, 243, 248; study, 111, 112, 114, 116, 117, 120, 124, 126, 127, 130, 132, 134

Cinchona alkaloids, 183–86, 199, 202, 256

Cinchona bark, 32, 189, 206, 207, 212, 236, 240, 256, 257; chemical content, 25, 143, 183, 198, 199, 200, 205; Europe (1650), 29; exportation controlled by Spain, 116; markets (*See* Amsterdam, London, Rome); price, 206. *See also* Peruvian bark

Cinchona bogotensis, 119

Cinchona calisaya, 143, 144, 145, 148, 149, 150, 151, 169, 172, 173, 174, 175, 176, 178, 182, 184, 190–93, 195, 198, 199, 200, 203, 214; quinine content, 169

Cinchona Export Ordinance, 225, 226

Cinchona ledgeriana, 198, 199, 200, 201, 204, 206, 207, 220, 238, 240, 258; cultivation process, 204–05, 214; Philippine culture, 238

Cinchona Planting Ordinance, 225–26

Cinchona succirubra (red cinchona), 180–84, 200, 201, 208, 257; cultivation, 231; Philippine culture, 239; quinine content, 184

Cinchonidine (alkaloid), 183

[268]

INDEX

INDEX

Paracelsus, 13, 14
Paris, 103, 160, 230
Pasteur, Louis, 153, 154, 156, 160, 162, 256
Patients (malarial), blood, 162; carriers, 167; India, 162; Russia, 162; tests of alkaloids, 185; United States, 162
Pavón (botanist), 124–25, 244
Pelletier, Pierre Joseph, 142, 143, 149, 184
Penicillin, 89, 161
Penick, S. B. and Company, New York City, 258
Pepys, Samuel, 15
Peru, 20–28, 32, 39, 40, 43, 48, 52, 96, 101, 127, 128, 143, 144, 146, 150, 173, 180, 207; cinchona plantations, 221, 226; U.S. mission to, 243
Peruvian bark, 39, 40–42, 45–47, 49–52, 54, 60, 62, 63, 70, 74, 85–87, 91, 93, 94, 97, 98, 141, 142; "a fraud," 45; botanical classification, 97; "dangerous," 45, 52, 60; Germany (1696), 94; "harmful," 92; medical profession, 44, 87, 104; medicinal properties, 39, 94; method of administering, 43, 44; opposition to, 93–94; papal territories, 50; prejudice, 43; remedy for fevers, 42; Roman Catholic Church, 43; theological controversy, 49–50; use for all fevers, 44; useless for fevers other than malaria, 94; variation in effectiveness, 94–95, 99; "worthless," 44, 46. See also Cinchona; Cinchona bark
Petrarch, 11
Peyer, Conrad, 94
Pharmacopoeia (seventeenth century), 17
Philippine Islands, 119, 235, 239–49; anti-malarial campaign, 237, 254; cinchona plantations, 237, 238, 240, 241, 257; guerrilleros, 236; malaria, 236–42, 246, 248; public health, 236
Physic, 88; practice, 66, 91

Physicians, 39; Peru (seventeenth century), 28–29, 92, 93; Roman, 43
Plague. See Black Death
Plants, curative, 25–29, 41, 177
Plasmochin (anti-malarial synthetic), 231, 246
Plempius, Vopiscus Fortunatus, 47–52, 60
Pliny the Younger, 7, 27
Poème du quinquina, Le (La Fontaine), 82
Polvos de la Condesa, los. See Countess' Powder
Pontine Marshes, 8
"Popish Plot," 74
Portuguese cinchona plantations, 187–88
"Powder of the Most Eminent Cardinal de Lugo," 43, 51, 53
Prejudice, 43, 48, 52, 56, 92
Protozoa, 162
Prujean, Dr., 56–58
Ptolemy, 6
Public health, 167, 211, 229; first campaign, 188; Peru (seventeenth century), 28
Puerto Rico, 225
Puno, 189, 190, 192
Purging, 8, 14, 15, 17, 23, 45, 59, 61, 67, 70, 73, 80, 87, 89, 141. See also Bleeding; Emetics

Quacks (empirics), 63, 65–69, 87, 90
Quarantine, 28
Quartan ague. See Fever
Quartan fever. See Fever
Quechua (Indians), 170–72, 190
Quinidine (alkaloid), 183
Quinine, 18, 31, 71, 75, 82, 88, 89, 92, 108, 111, 114, 120, 127, 137, 138, 140, 141, 142, 151, 161, 183, 184, 214, 229, 233, 238, 240, 242, 243, 245, 246, 248, 256, 257, 258; administration, 82, 85–88, 93, 126; cheap, 219, 220, 221; chemical synthesis, 255; clinical study (malaria), 127; confusion as to properties, 127; cure for malaria only,